THE SCIENCE AND CULTURE SERIES

Rev. Joseph Husslein, S.J., Editor

THE SEVEN GOLDEN CITIES

Fray Marcos and the
Coronado Adventure

THE SEVEN GOLDEN CITIES

by

Mabel Farnum

THE BRUCE PUBLISHING COMPANY
MILWAUKEE

To

Rev. Pax R. Schicker, O.F.M.,
*Who Taught Me to Know and Love the Southwest
and Who Inspired This Book*

PREFACE BY THE GENERAL EDITOR

AN AIR OF mystery lingers about the title of this book and through it wafts the atmosphere of romance. It is the old lure of gold and treasures which more than four hundred years ago made the most daring and adventurous spirits of New Spain go in quest of the Seven Golden Cities.

The great explorers of that day, men like Cortés and De Soto, vied with each other for leadership in this undertaking.

As yet no white man ever had set eyes upon the walls of those mysterious cities. But the Indian tales, reported constantly from every side, were all sufficiently concordant. There could be no doubt, it seemed, as to the underlying truth, however much the stories might have gained in the retelling.

For what could have appeared too marvelous to the men of that generation who themselves had witnessed the conquests of Mexico and Peru? Why might not this be the climax of all adventures?

Gold, glory, and of course, new realms for Spain: these were the impelling incentives. Nor was religion forgotten. For the sturdy Spanish conquistadores, though they loved the earth and all its goods — not seldom over much — were no materialists. They acknowledged at least the need of pagans to be Christianized and souls to be saved. Gold, glory, and a crusade! What Spaniard could fail to be moved by one or all of these motives, vaguely blended though they might be in the minds of many! The point never to be forgotten of course is that Christian motives cannot justify wrongful deeds.

As we turn to read the story of this book, there pass before us vividly the tribes and races of the great Southwest, as four centuries ago Fray Marcos looked on them.

Next, across the vast stage of shining mesa and volcanic hills, come riding on in flashing steel the cavaliers of Coronado, the sunlight blazing from their shields and armored steeds. Following close upon them are the men-at-arms, marching, marching, marching, over endless routes, under fiery skies, over cactus-covered deserts.

Gold, glory, Spain — and souls to save!

It is a panoramic picture. But what lends particular interest to the book is the variety of clearly drawn characters we meet with here — bold, ardent, strenuous men, such as Spain bred in those days; men who never recked the cost and danger, nor counted the piled-up odds against them, but rode straight through, to victory or death.

Most notable in all this company are three personalities, each uniquely different from the others.

First is the friar, Fray Marcos de Niza, selected to act as herald to the seven cities, and lead the important reconnoitering expedition sent out by the Spanish Crown. With the exception of the first few stages of the journey, he is the only white man in the entire group, made up largely of Indians attracted to him from almost all the islands and villages along the route. A lithe, kindly, gentle, gray-robed figure, he moves about untroubled among the motley crowd, a subdued fire of heroic determination burning in his eyes, and an insuperable sense of duty urging him on, eager only for God and souls.*

---

* Passing allusion may here be made to a questioning of the veracity of Fray Marcos on the part of a few recent writers. Naturally this controversy has no place in the book. Suffice it to say that the author's interpretation is perfectly rationalized, sympathetic and consistent throughout, conforming to the testimony given the friar by the two best qualified judges: the great Bishop Juan de Zumárraga and the friar's own Provincial.

The second person to be remembered is the gallant, youthful General in command of the military expedition that was next to follow, Don Francisco Vásquez de Coronado. True lover and brave soldier underneath his gilded armor, he is faithful to the ideals of chivalry as he conceives of them, despite weaknesses and failure, so far as we follow him here. Buoyantly he sets out on his desperate undertaking that ends as he little dreamed. Yet his name was not written in water and he permanently holds his niche in history.

Last and most astonishing personage in this trio is Estevan the Moor — half mountebank, half genius — loaned by his master to serve as interpreter to Fray Marcos. Ebony-featured, hawk-eyed, with long black beard that waves in the wind, he is the admiration of the natives. His shrewdness no less than his clowning, and the glowing recital of his own imaginary deeds — undaunted and resourceful though he actually was — still more fascinates them. No one could fathom, no one could trust him. His vices like his antics are legion. Violating explicit orders, he enters in gaudy costume the first of the seven cities, anticipating the friar's arrival, and there meets his tragic end. Yet his heart is not all black, as the author observes, for in it are spots of tenderness for Fray Marcos, who deeply deplores his death. But the fate of both the friar's and Coronado's own expedition were linked up with him. And so three men, in all the world the most unlike each other, forever remain united in the annals of world history.

There are other characters in this vivid narrative no less distinctly limned than the three just mentioned — men of heroic stature, such as the viceroy himself, Don Antonio de Mendoza; the straightforward, hard-fighting captain Melchior Díaz; the truly great Bishop Juan de Zumárraga, defender of the rights of the natives; and, to proceed no further, Don García López de Cárdenas, who covered with his own body the prostrate form of his leader, struck down in the assault on Hawikuh.

But a specially notable service is rendered the lay reader by the opportunity offered him of acquiring a better and more intimate knowledge of a large and most interesting section of America. In colorful and picturesque ways are described for him its geological marvels, its wonderful plant life and the amazing scenery that here astonishes the beholder. Ethnologically accurate accounts are also given of the various native tribes of the Southwest, their skills in peace and war, their family life, their morals and religious beliefs. We enter the huts of the natives and are made familiar with them.

Naturally, to render possible the scientific background to this book, repeated visits of research to the region in question were required, not to mention the vast reading of contemporary and more recent works. But sufficient reference to all this will be found in the author's own "Acknowledgments."

So, off to the Seven Golden Cities!

Joseph Husslein, S.J., Ph.D.,
General Editor, Science and Culture Series

St. Louis University,
March, 1943

ACKNOWLEDGMENTS

The data for The SEVEN GOLDEN CITIES was gathered from all available sources, early and modern, carefully compared and utilized as needed for the purposes of this book. These sources include the *Reports of the Bureau of American Ethnology* which form the historical, geographical and ethnological groundwork; principally the *Narrative of Pedro de Castañeda,* secretary of the Coronado Expedition, by George Parker Winship, and the "Letters" of Viceroy Mendoza and Coronado as contained in the *Reports.*

Narratives of the Coronado Expedition, Hammond and Rey, University of New Mexico Press, were combed for the latest findings in this field. Other source material comprised the writings of Adolph Bandelier, Charles Lummis and contemporary writers on the Southwest, also Brebner's *North American Explorers* and the papers of Professor Lansing B. Bloom, University of New Mexico, whose scholarly investigations and findings, particularly in relation to Fray Marcos de Niza, were of great inspiration and assistance.

The volumes of the Bureau of American Ethnology were consulted for matter on the native tribes of Old Mexico and our Southwest, also the works of Bancroft and the studies published by the University of California Press.

The description of the architecture and customs of the Zuni Indians presented by Victor Mindeleff, with his ground plans of Hawikuh Pueblo, was supplemented by a reconnaissance made by the author in September, 1941, on the ruins of the Indian village of the sixteenth century.

Spanish texts were used in the preparation of the work; also, in lesser degree, Italian and French, for the purpose of obtaining as accurate a picture of times, events and personalities as possible.

To the following distinguished gentlemen who helped to make this book possible, I offer heartfelt gratitude:

Rev. John F. Bannon, S.J., Department of History, St. Louis University, who directed my reading and furnished me with most valuable helps in relation to the study of Old Mexico and the Coronado Expedition.

Rev. Peter M. Dunne, S.J., historian, San Francisco University, for meteorological data and other assistance in my research during a visit to the West Coast.

Rev. W. Eugene Shiels, S.J., formerly of the Department of History of Loyola University, Chicago, Illinois, now an associate editor of *America,* who was the first to come to my aid in the matter of the Fray Marcos controversy.

Rev. Jerome Hesse, O.F.M., formerly of the Cathedral of Saint Francis of Assisi, Sante Fé, New Mexico, now pastor of Sacred Heart Cathedral, Gallup, New Mexico, for his tireless activity in behalf of the work.

Rev. Pax R. Schicker, O.F.M., Chancellor of the Diocese of Gallup, New Mexico, and Rev. Eugene Spoerl, O.F.M., formerly of Saint Anthony's Indian Mission, Zuni, New Mexico, now assistant pastor of St. Clement Church, Cincinnati, Ohio, my companions at Hawikuh in a memorable experience exploring on the ruins of the ancient Indian settlement.

Professor Lansing B. Bloom, University of New Mexico, whose generous interest in this book was climaxed during a visit of the author to his "workshop" at Albuquerque, when I was privileged to examine precious documents dealing with Fray Marcos de Niza, brought by Professor Bloom from Spain.

The purpose of The SEVEN GOLDEN CITIES is to make known and revered a Franciscan herald and pioneer of four centuries ago, whose heroic sacrifices formed the first link in a missionary chain extending to our day; also, to promote the noble cause of the missions to the Indians, the first Americans, who, when they receive the light of faith, make fervent converts and exemplary children of the Church.

IN THE GOVERNMENT palace at Mexico City, Don Antonio de Mendoza, first viceroy of "New Spain," *Nueva España*, sat at table with three unusual guests, haggard, sunbrowned wanderers. The month was August; the year, 1536.

Many strangers had been welcomed at the viceroy's board since the beginning of his administration in November of the previous year. The majority were restless adventurers — men indeed of the best blood of Spain, but waiting only for official license to set out on enterprises that might net them political prestige or material treasure. To encourage their ambitions for conquest, in their own interest and that of the Crown, was the viceroy's motive in his dealing with them.

Of all his visitors none had so strongly wrought on his imagination and influenced his action as the three guests now seated at his table. From Culiacán in the Sinaloa country, stretching along the west coast of Mexico, they had traveled south to Compostela, a city founded by the Spanish conquistadores the previous year and named for the church in the mother country which enshrined the relics of the illustrious patron of Spain, Saint James. Thence they had journeyed inland in a southeasterly direction to the capital, to report their adventures to the viceroy.

1

As Don Antonio listened intently to their story, he was aware that it was more weird and provocative than any he had ever heard.

A fourth member of the group, a black-faced Moor, was lodged for the time with the Pima Indians in the viceroy's menage. The other three were Spaniards: Alvar Núñez Cabeza de Vaca, a native of Xeres de la Fontera in Spain, and later a resident of Seville; Andrés de Dorantes, of Bejar; and Alonso del Castillo Maldonado, of Salamanca. To the second of these men belonged the Moor, Estevan, whose name bore the adjunct "de Dorantes," implying he was the property of Dorantes.

Together, these four were the sole survivors of an expedition that had been financed by the Spanish Crown, and was placed under the command of Pánfilo Narváez, "the one-eyed," who had lost his other eye in an unfortunate encounter with the conqueror of Mexico, Hernando Cortés.

The band of explorers had set out from Spain to seek new territory for the mother country across the seas. Approximately six hundred souls daringly embarked on that epochal voyage, which was to prove so tragically disappointing.

They sailed from Spain on June 27, 1527. After many vicissitudes they were shipwrecked on the Texas coast. Thence they struggled onward amid untold misfortunes until only the four now enjoying the viceroy's hospitality remained to push on across the country and find their way back to civilization. Among the lost was a band of Franciscan friars who had joined the enterprise in the hope of converting to Christianity some, at least, of the primitive peoples of the New World.

Westward the four survivors trudged, across Texas; Chihuahua — a northern province of Mexico — and Sonora, another province lying to the west, until they reached what was then the extreme northernmost settlement of the Spaniards on the Pacific Coast, Culiacán.

The secretary of the Narváez expedition, Alvar Núñez Cabeza de Vaca, was now recounting the details of the voyage from Spain to the New World. He had just arrived at the point of his narrative where the fleet was still intact and had reached Santo Domingo.

"It was there," he continued, "that about one fourth of our company deserted, choosing to remain with the islanders. So, then, we left them there, and after procuring the necessary horses and supplies, sailed for Santiago, Cuba, where again we increased our stock.

"The next port reached was Vera Cruz. Here I received orders to take two of the ships and proceed to Trinidad, while Narváez remained at the former port. My duty was to secure still further supplies.

"Arrived at Trinidad I went ashore with thirty of my men. But we had gone only a short distance when a terrible storm arose. So fierce and dreadful was the velocity of the wind that we locked ourselves together, seven or eight in a row, lest we be blown away. Churches and dwellings went down in the terrible hurricane, as well as the tall trees.

"After a night of terror we made our way back to the shore.

"In the branches of a tree that had withstood the storm we sighted the remnants of one of our small boats. Farther on we came across the bodies of two of our seamen, but so torn and disfigured that we could not establish their identity. That, with some broken box covers and a tattered cape and quilt, was all we ever saw again of our two ships and of the brave men who manned them.

"Several days passed and at last the Narváez fleet arrived. Fortunately it had lain safe in harbor."

Rising as he spoke, Cabeza de Vaca strode up and down the room, gesticulating vigorously, and flinging out his arms in graphic motions. It was then that Don Antonio de Mendoza noticed that the tips of his guest's fingers were worn down almost to stubs. The explanation of this the viceroy was soon to learn, as De Vaca went on:

"We now set out with Narváez, but misfortune lay in wait for us. Just beyond the western extremity of Cuba our ships became stranded on the shoals. When at last they floated again we sailed for fifteen days, only to run once more into further storms. Unable to enter the bay of Havana, owing to a strong south wind, we pointed our prows for Florida. This we sighted on April 12. Some Indians were visible on the shore and we traded with them a few trinkets for sorely needed venison and fish."

Eventually, at a point later to be known as Tampa Bay, Narváez went ashore with his men and took possession of a village that looked to be deserted. The inhabitants had fled inland on seeing the ships.

"This proved to be another disappointment, for just then we were in bad need of provisions. Nearly half of our horses had died and the rest were so weak as to be practically useless. . . . The day was Good Friday, and we made our devotions as best we could under these circumstances."

The emaciated bronzed countenance of De Vaca assumed a reverential expression, which was reflected on the faces of his companions as he repeated the last words. But Don Antonio needed no such evidence to understand how strong was the faith in the souls of these hardy adventurous sons of the Church.

At this point in his narrative, the speaker reached his climax, insignificant as the incident which he mentioned might appear in itself.

In one of the houses left tenantless by the Indians in

their flight the Spaniards found a small gold ornament, obviously dropped by someone in the hasty retreat.

Gold!

It was the magic word that kindled high the hopes of every Spaniard of that day and moved him to undertake heroic feats of endurance. Even in the thin sallow cheeks of Mendoza rose a flush of excitement.

De Vaca spoke on.

"This determined Narváez. He would strike for the north and see whether gold might not be found there. Indeed, the Indians assured him that in a place called Appalachen the metal abounded.

"In vain I tried to persuade him to abandon his plan. It was to send the fleet up the coast in search of a favorable harbor, while he with his officers would press inland in search of the wealthy town.

" 'If you do so,' I warned him, 'you will never again see your ships.' My words were of no avail. With forty armored men, astride of armored horses, and with five friars going on foot, the rest of the army following, Narváez set out to penetrate the thickets of Florida. Meanwhile the ships sailed to find a favorable harbor."

Enduring great hardship from lack of food, and pressed down by the weight of their armor, the party at last reached Appalachen, on St. John's Day, June 24, 1528.

"Your lordship," De Vaca continued, turning to Don Antonio, "can well imagine their chagrin when they discovered at their journey's end nothing more than a poor settlement of about forty clay huts. Vainly searching the vicinity for anything of promise, they finally reached Appalachen Bay."

But the ships?

"They were nowhere to be seen. Only a smooth expanse of shining ocean greeted the bewildered eyes of Narváez and his men."

Here was tragedy.

Boats were a necessity, and in order to fashion them out of hides, the horses had to be killed. But that was necessary, since the men had to appease their hunger.

Thanks to the inventiveness of the group, they succeeded in building the small crafts needed, and that without tools, or iron, or forge, or resin, or rigging. Everything available was requisitioned. Wooden tubes and deerskin, iron from the stirrup, crossbows and spurs, pitch from the pine trees, palmetto fiber and horsehair — all these were utilized by the one carpenter in the company, aided by his numerous raw recruits.

"At last we had five boats, twenty-one cubits long," went on De Vaca, "and so, after we had eaten the flesh of the last of our horses, we set sail, without any of us knowing how to man the crafts.

"By this time our small expeditionary force had been sadly depleted. Ten men had died from the arrows of the Indians who attacked us, and forty from sickness or starvation. Yet eventually we came in sight of the Mississippi River."

From that time on, however, misfortune stalked the hapless Spaniards. Four of their five boats were wrecked. Only that commanded by Narváez remained afloat. Soon it, too, met with the same fate, and the intrepid commander with his fearless followers went down into a watery grave. He had been a brave, but not always judicious man.

De Vaca himself and his three companions, including the Moorish slave, had been cast on the shores of Texas in the wreck of their craft, and taken captive by the Indians. Six years of painful slavery followed before they succeded in escaping. Sometimes separately, for fear of the enemy, sometimes in a group, they now made their way from tribe to tribe. Crossing the western part of the state, they next cut though portions of New Mexico and Arizona, and so made directly for Sonora, in northern Mexico. In the spring of 1536 they reached Culiacán, to the south, in central Sinaloa.

Referring to some of the events of this long and perilous journey, De Vaca mentioned an island named by the wanderers Malhado, or "Misfortune," because of the dangers and sufferings they had endured. They were infinitely surprised when the natives regarded them as medicine men, with power to cure their sick.

"We protested that we were not," De Vaca said. "But this did not satisfy the Indians. They refused to give us any food until we agreed to do as they wished. So we made the Sign of the Cross over the infirm and ailing they brought to us, and we recited a *Pater Noster* and *Ave Maria* over each one, asking God to cure them if He so willed. Providentially for us, as for them, the sick Indians got well. All the tribe believed we had wrought the cure, and were deeply impressed by our 'powers.' "

Again Mendoza was moved to edification by the recital of De Vaca, whose humble trust in Divine Providence and diffidence in himself had been so singularly rewarded.

De Vaca forbore to state that during a severe illness which he had suffered while on this island, his present compatriots, Maldonado and Dorantes, had deserted him in his hour of need, as had also the Moor, Estevan.

Instead, he held up his hands that the viceroy might see more plainly the wounds that disfigured them.

"Your lordship has noticed the condition of my hands. Other Indians were not so favorable to me, and while I remained on the island, for more than a year, they treated me cruelly. I was forced to labor among the canebrakes, pulling up the roots that could be utilized for food. Soon my hands were raw and bleeding, and my entire body bruised and cut by the harsh brakes.

"Happily I made my escape, and going inland, met a tribe of Cahrucos. There I became transformed into a trader, whose wares were sea shells and cockles brought from the shore. These I bartered for hides, canes and flints to make arrows, red ocher and similar articles of which I should have need."

At this Dorantes intervened.

"Speaking of arrows," he said, "in one of the Indian villages the natives gave me arrows made of emeralds. When I asked whence they came I was told from a mountainous country lying to the north. Here, they said, were many houses of goodly size. The villages where we received this information we named Corazones (Hearts), because the Indians gave us hearts of deer to eat."

Here De Vaca recalled something of like nature, but even more remarkable.

While wandering across the Texas plains, he stated, the natives informed him of a rich country lying to the north, doubtless the same Dorantes had just mentioned.

"They said nothing about gold to be found in these cities," he continued, "but they did speak of them as rich and populous, and said that silversmiths plied their trade in the streets.

"This was not, however, entirely new. For as early as 1527, when Nuño de Guzmán ruled at Pánuco, an Indian told him a story of seven populous cities lying to the northwest. This tale came to be widely accepted throughout Mexico. Guzmán himself was so eager to find these cities that he actually started in search of them, but gave up the quest when he had gone as far as the southern part of Sonora.

"Shortly before we ourselves started on our journey to find these cities, some Indians presented us with a hawk bell made of copper. It was large and thick, and had a face carved upon it. When later we crossed the Rio

Grande, we met still other natives to whom we showed the bell and they assured us that a great amount of metal similar to it lay buried in the soil in the place from which it came. They also said that many lofty habitations were in the place, and other treasure, well worth securing.

"Very large pearls and similar precious things were to be found on the coast of the South Sea [the Pacific] they stated, also that the cities in that locality were the largest and richest of any on the continent."

Don Antonio de Mendoza, viceroy of His Majesty's territory of Nueva España, had heard sufficient for his purpose. He was well satisfied to excuse his guests and permit them to seek a little rest, for they were still worn and weary after the bitter experiences of the past.

One request he had to make before dismissing them — he had no thought it would be refused. Addressing Andrés de Dorantes, he said:

"From my Indians I have learned that this Moor who travels in your company is well versed in the various Indian dialects, as well as in the Indian sign language. I could use him to great advantage here. What do you say to selling him to me?"

Mendoza clapped his hands, and an Indian servant appeared, bearing a gold plate on which rested a large sum of money. At a sign from the viceroy, he placed the plate in front of Dorantes.

The latter, however, did not seem greatly interested in it. He shook his head, as he replied:

"Estevan is very useful to me. I would not part with him for any amount."

Mendoza insisted on his point. When Dorantes again declined to comply with the request, the viceroy said:

"If you will lease him to me, I promise you that he will be well treated and returned after a certain length of time on which we both shall agree. What do you say to that?"

Still loath to comply with the request, but unwilling to offend or disappoint the hospitable viceroy, Dorantes consented to this arrangement, although with no alacrity.

When the three Spaniards had left his presence, Don Antonio sought his private chamber, to think over the stupendous project that had flashed across his keen and far-seeing mind as a result of De Vaca's stirring relation.

Rich and populous cities lying to the north. . . . Seven Golden Cities, filled with treasure, at present known only to ignorant and superstitious Indians, who could not possibly realize its value or significance!

Why should not these cities be conquered, in the Name of the Divine Majesty, and that of the Spanish sovereign?

Every indication seemed to point to the desirability of the mighty venture.

Now came the all-important problem:

Whom to charge with the fortunes of the expedition which should journey, with the benediction of Divine Providence and the favor of the king, to that land shrouded in mystery, whose riches must be acquired for a noble cause; whose people would receive, in return for their submission, the Faith of Jesus Christ, a gift beyond price or computation?

Almost instantaneously Mendoza arrived at the solution of the matter.

There was one man for whose talents the task was eminently fitted.

This man was the youthful Don Francisco Vásquez de Coronado, whom the viceroy had brought over with him from Spain to be his secretary when he came to assume his viceregal post in the colonial possessions of the mother country across the seas.

Don Francisco was at present engaged in active preparations for the conduct of military operations in a mining district under the jurisdiction of the viceroy, where the

Negroes were showing signs of unrest which was soon to grow into an open rebellion. While this affair was under surveillance, the viceroy himself would open the necessary negotiations with the king, in order to win his consent to the sending of an expedition to the north. Both affairs would require time — but Mendoza was satisfied to move slowly, in order not to jeopardize the success of the project.

The cost of outfitting such an expedition would necessarily be enormous. Unless some verification of the stories told by the Indians concerning the seven rich cities could be first obtained, His Majesty could hardly be expected to consent to the venture, nor would the viceroy be willing to risk his reputation on it.

What, then, was he to do that he might pave the way for the dispatch of an army to the north? Here another idea came to the fertile brain of Mendoza — it was no less happy than the former.

He had a friend in Mexico, a revered and illustrious churchman, who would be certain to suggest an expedient in the dilemma. This friend was the bishop of Mexico, Juan de Zumárraga, whose holiness and wisdom were undisputed by any.

Often in the monastery of Zeptharztec the good bishop, a delightful saint, had conversed with Mendoza on the interests of the Faith and those of their country. He would be able to recommend someone competent to undertake the difficult and delicate role of pioneer and herald, blazing a trail far to the north and confirming the tales of the seven rich cities told by the Indians.

Over that trail, if plans worked out, as Mendoza was determined they should, a valiant army of Spaniards, with a young courageous general at their head, should journey to find the glittering cities and take them for God and for Spain.

IN THE NARROW STREETS of Mexico City a busy hum of life stirred in the drowsy afternoon. Jostling one another, Spaniards, Indians and Negroes passed to and fro. Helping still more effectually to block the way, mules dragged misshapen little carts through the mud that lay deep wherever the numerous canals intersecting the city had overflowed. An occasional horseman — horses were costly and therefore few in Mexico — guided a handsome Andalusian mount through the maze of moving figures.

In the privacy of his chamber, Viceroy Mendoza conversed with his young protégé, Don Francisco Vásquez de Coronado. Two years had elapsed since the dramatic appearance of Alvar Núñez Cabeza de Vaca and his companions at the court of Nueva España.

"I found it somewhat difficult to reach here, your lordship," Don Francisco said. "The roads are in bad condition."

Mendoza nodded assent. "I know," he replied. "My Indian workers are employed continuously in repairing the broken dikes, but, as you are aware, these people are lazy and disinclined to persevere in a task unless they are goaded to do it. However, I have no intention to imitate my 'good friend' Hernando Cortés, who made it a practice to use severe measures in dealing with them. I believe our ends can be best served by employing persuasive methods. It is a slow process, I grant you. Yet we have succeeded in opening up a good many roads leading to the ports and mines. Over them I intend to send missionaries, one of these days, to Christianize the tribes to the north of us."

Don Antonio's thin face, with its keen dark eyes and decisive mouth shadowed by a black pointed beard and drooping mustachios, indicated a man of courage and accomplishment. His high forehead was deeply lined, for he slept but little, and the period of his repose was frequently broken as, for instance, when a messenger arrived with news of an affair in some part of his dominion requiring his immediate attention. Ever alert to serve the interests of Church and state, he invariably listened with patience and interest to every detail of the business, then acted on the information as he deemed expedient.

On the borders of Granada, within the grim walls of a mountain fortress, Don Antonio de Mendoza had first seen the light of this world. He could trace his lineage to patrician nobles and Gothic dukes of Cantabria. His father, Inigo López de Mendoza, second Conde de Tendilla and Captain General of the Christian forces, had his headquarters at Alcalá de Real when this son was born.

Over seventy different titles indicating distinction were borne by members of his family. Statesmen, writers, soldiers, defenders of the Holy See, they had received alike from Roman pontiffs and kings singular marks of appreciation and esteem. In his young manhood Don Antonio distinguished himself in military feats. Later he served as imperial ambassador to Hungary until the early part of 1528, when he returned to Madrid. In autumn of the following year he accepted the offer of his Queen, whose chamberlain he was, to become head of the government of Nueva España.

The office of viceroy was created as an expedient in an uncomfortable situation which had disturbed the Spanish sovereign greatly. The intrepid but rash and overambitious Cortés had wrested Mexico from the Aztecs. Now he was seeking to increase his prestige and maintain the power to which he felt himself entitled by reason of his stupendous achievement.

But — and Mendoza was thoroughly in agreement with this policy — the home government was chary of entrusting too much authority to one who had wrought strongly upon public opinion and had gained the favor of his countrymen in territory belonging to Spain, yet which was removed from her by the span of a mighty ocean. Surely it was the part of wisdom to check the inordinate advances of Cortés, and if possible without incurring resentment on his part. The bestowal of a high-sounding title upon him, while taking the reins of government out of his hands, was accomplished successfully. Created Marques del Valle, Cortés was none the less disappointed, embittered, and determined to regain his lost authority and prestige.

His feelings toward the viceroy were, naturally, far from friendly. Mendoza was fully aware of this situation, but he had no intention of allowing it to thwart his plans for the promotion of the king's interests and the good of the realm.

As they talked together, the viceroy and Don Francisco Vásquez de Coronado were thinking of Cortés. Both men realized that the disgruntled conquistador entertained an overweening desire to accomplish the very thing they were resolved to accomplish — an expedition to the north in quest of the lordly cities which Alvar Núñez Cabeza de Vaca had described so glowingly.

The mention by the viceroy, therefore, of "tribes to the north of us," brought a flush of animation and desire to the countenances of both men.

Don Antonio de Mendoza had now received definite

news regarding his immediate plans and meant to disclose these developments to Don Francisco.

"We have found the man whom we shall dispatch north on a reconnaissance, and whose report shall determine our first move," he said. "He is a Franciscan, Fray Marcos de Niza, vice-commissary of his Order in Nueva España. My revered friend, Bishop Zumárraga, brought him here to see me, and we talked matters over and arrived at our decision.

"Fray Marcos is the herald and pioneer who shall pave the way for our glorious triumph in the far north. Listen, Francisco, while I read you a copy of a letter which the bishop sent in April of last year to an ecclesiastic in Mexico, in which he speaks of the qualities of Fray Marcos:

" 'This Father,' says the bishop of him, 'is a deeply religious person, worthy of credit, of approved virtue and of much religion and zeal. The friars in Peru elected him as *custodio*. On leaving there, some of them came to us, after having noted the evil deeds and cruelties of men who are called Christians. He [Fray Marcos] wrote me from Guatemala. I took him to see the viceroy, and his lordship sent on to the King and the Council the relation made by him. As he and all the friars are so much occupied in sermons and confessions, nothing could be done until the present, when in haste some few accounts are going forward, in which he speaks as an eyewitness.

" 'Your Reverence,' the bishop further addresses the Mexican ecclesiastic, 'has to give a written copy of these two documents into the hands of the Emperor, communicating it by means of Dr. Bernal, who should strongly endeavor to persuade his Catholic heart that these conquests which are so injurious to our Christianity and Catholic faith should be stopped. In all this land there has been nothing but slaughter for as many conquests as have been made; and if His Majesty should commit this affair to the Viceroy, Don Antonio de Mendoza, I think that they would cease, and what shall be discovered may be conquered in an apostolic and Christian manner.' "

Having completed the reading of Bishop Zumárraga's letter, Mendoza addressed Coronado:

"Fray Marcos has traveled extensively, and has undergone many hardships and perils in his adventurous career. Coming here from his native Savoy, he labored for a time at Santo Domingo, then passed on to Peru. There he joined the forces of Francisco Pizarro. He was a witness to the execution of the young Inca prince, Atahualpa, at Caxamalca. This incident must have been a painful trial to the friar, since he has always been deeply interested in the well-being of the Indians.

"I understand that Fray Marcos is well versed in the arts of navigation, and it is said that he has written and published works dealing with the natives of Peru and Quito. I found him to be as he was described to me — a man of peace-loving nature, gentle and sympathetic. Bishop Zumárraga and his own provincial, Fray Antonio Cuidad-Rodrigo, speak in highest terms of his character and qualifications.

"Fray Marcos de Niza is the man whom we shall dispatch north, Francisco, when spring renders the roads passable, to discover what lies beyond and to prepare the way for our great adventure."

The viceroy and the young soldier spent some time in more minute discussion of the all-important subject, before passing on to other topics.

Complimented by his chief for putting down an insurrection of Negroes in the mining district of Amatepeque, Don Francisco left the viceroy's presence, well satisfied with his new appointment and ready to prepare for his present departure for Nueva Galicia. This province he was to govern until it would be time to organize the expedition to march into the north.

Left alone in his chamber, Don Antonio pondered on the project of the expedition, and on the role which the Franciscan friar, Marcos de Niza, was to fulfill in it.

Out in the open, in the great markets of the city, merchants were crying their wares in raucous voices. People of every age and station crowded the long succession of stalls running the entire length of the plaza and displaying commodities of every kind. Many of these commodities found their way to the viceroy's household, which Mendoza conducted on a lavish scale, chiefly by means of the revenue accruing from his sheep ranches.

To the market traders from all adjacent parts came to sell or barter their goods. Goldsmiths, potters, jewelers, stonecutters, chair and mat makers, tailors, apothecaries, sellers of fish and pastry vied for the patronage of those who came by. The shops of the tradesmen who sold the more massive materials, such as lime, stone, timber, and the like, were located in the adjacent streets.

Beneath Mendoza's window, in the once magnificent gardens of the Moctezumas, native servants moved about at their daily chores, crossing and recrossing the numerous intersecting paths laid in glistening pebbles and the formally designed patios beside which ran channels for irrigation.

Usually there was no need to send to the market for medicinal supplies. In a remote corner of the gardens curative plants and aromatic herbs were carefully cultivated. Innumerable bundles of these, after being dried in the sun, were stored in the closets of the house, to be brought forth when any member of the household showed signs of indisposition. Every Spanish family was fully acquainted with their medicinal qualities. Even certain species of cacti yielded properties highly useful for healing purposes.

Out of sight, at a little distance from these beds, were the utilitarian gardens. Here Mendoza's Indians, of whom he maintained sixty on the premises, tended the vegetables and fruits and conveyed them to the cooks, as needed, for the table.

Don Antonio de Mendoza was particularly pleased to realize that many products of the gardens, once employed in the superstitious rites of the Aztecs, now conduced toward the comfort and well-being of "Christians." And so, too, many of the rare species of flowers, whose odors ascended to his windows, were previously known under pagan names that now had long since given way to others rich in meaning to the Spaniards, reminding them of their cherished faith and the land of their birth and predilection.

In the viceroy's gardens exotic trees lifted their branches like praying arms. One of the most popular bore a flower called in Aztec *Yoloxochitl*, but known to the "Christians" as the "heartflower." A single petal of this blossom sufficed to perfume an entire house. Formerly only Aztec nobles might possess it. Highly valued curative properties were ascribed to it.

At present, however, Don Antonio was chiefly concerned to put upon paper his directions that should guide the Savoyard friar, Marcos de Niza, who was to act as herald for the journey northward in quest of a great prize for Spain. They were instructions of tact and diplomacy with which each expedition was to be prefaced.

"Fray Marcos de Niza": the viceroy began his letter, "This is what you must do in the expedition you are undertaking for the honor and glory of the Holy Trinity, and for the propagation of our holy Catholic Faith:

"First — as soon as you arrive at the province of Culicán you shall encourage and exhort the Spaniards, who reside in the town of San Miguel, to treat well the Indians who are at peace and not to employ them in excessive tasks, assuring them that if they do so, they shall find favor with and be rewarded by His Majesty for the labors which they have undergone, and in me they shall have a good supporter for their claims, but if they do the contrary, they shall be punished and out of favor.

"As for the Indians, you shall give them to understand that I send you in the name of his Majesty, in order that they be treated well, and may know that he is afflicted by the affronts and injuries which they have received. Let them understand that henceforth they shall be well treated, and that those who do them harm shall be punished.

"Likewise, you shall assure them that they shall no longer be slaves, nor removed from their lands, but shall be left free to dwell on them without hurt or damage. Let them lose their fear and recognize God, our Lord, who is in heaven, and the emperor, who is placed by His hand on earth to rule and govern it.

"And as Francisco Vásquez de Coronado, whom His Majesty has appointed governor of that province, will go with you to the town of San Miguel of Culiacán, you must advise me how he provides for the affairs of that town, in what concerns the service of God, our Lord, and the conversion and good treatment of the natives of that province.

"And if by the aid of God, our Lord, and the grace of the Holy Ghost, you shall find a way to go farther and to enter the country beyond, you shall take with you Stephen [Estevan] Dorantes for a guide, whom I order that he obey you in all and by all that you command him, as he would himself, and if he does not do so, he shall be in jeopardy, and shall incur the penalties which befall those who do not obey persons who hold power from His Majesty to command them.

"Likewise the said governor, Francisco Vásquez, has with him the Indians who came with Dorantes, and some others that it has been possible to gather from these parts, in order that, if to him and to you both it may seem advisable that you take some in your company, you may do so and use them as you see fit for the service of our Lord.

"You shall always arrange to go in the safest manner possible, and inform yourself first if the Indians be at peace or war with one another, that you may give them no occasion to commit any indiscretion against your person, which would be the cause of proceeding against them and chastizing them. If such were the case, instead of doing them good and bringing them light, the result would be just the opposite.

"You shall take care, great care, to observe the people whom you meet, whether they be many or few, and note if they are scattered or live close together. . . ."

The viceroy then gave the friar explicit directions concerning the recognition of the country through which he was to pass, after which he continued his letter as follows:

"Always arrange to send news by the Indians telling how you fare and are received and particularly what you may find.

"And if God, our Lord, be pleased that you find some large town, which may seem to you well situated for the establishment of a monastery, dispatch to that place some religious to undertake the work of conversion. Send word by the Indians, or return yourself to Culiacán. . . .

"And, although all the earth belongs to the Emperor, our lord, you, in my name, shall take possession of the country for His Majesty, and you shall erect the signs and perform the acts which shall seem to you to be required in such a case. Further, you shall give the natives of the

country to understand that there is a God in heaven and the Emperor on the earth, to command and govern it, to whom all men must be subject, and whom all must serve."
— Don Antonio de Mendoza.

When he had affixed his signature to the document, the viceroy leaned back in his chair and breathed a sigh of relief. He believed that the written orders for the friar were clear and explicit. He was satisfied that they would be obeyed.

The journey of Fray Marcos de Niza, as Mendoza well knew, would be lonely and filled with sufferings. It would be dangerous, too, for the four survivors of the ill-fated Narváez expedition had made that amply plain to him. However, he did not intend to send Fray Marcos north without a white companion. Provision for this exigency had already been made with the help of the Father Provincial of the Franciscans. Fray Onorato, a lay brother, pious and amiable, was to accompany him on the way.

Estevan's guidance and influence would ensure a less difficult and dangerous journey for the friars than it might otherwise be. The Moor exercised a certain influence over the Indians, and his talents as interpreter were considerable. Besides, he was to act in the capacity of scout for the enterprise, going on before his party at certain stages and preparing the unknown tribes for the coming of the white men.

Estevan was afraid of nothing, as Mendoza had occasion to know. His audacity had often caused the Spaniards about the viceroy's palace to complain bitterly of him. However, in the wilderness through which he must pass, as well as in the Indian hamlets, he could hardly get into serious mischief — so at least Mendoza innocently thought. And Fray Marcos de Niza was to have full authority over the Moor, and make known to the viceroy any misdemeanor on his part.

The viceroy closed his eyes, the better to visualize the entire picture in perspective:

A lonely man, in dusty gray robe; barefoot, with the desert sun drenching his frail form; trudging over the spiny cacti that thrust out menacing arms to wound him; climbing with bruised feet the stony hills, facing the biting winds that swept down upon him; watching, it might be, in some native settlement, the frenzied Indians dancing about poles on which were strung the gruesome trophies of war; and last, but not least, evading the flight of poisoned arrows aimed at him. All this the viceroy's imagination could conjure up.

Anything might happen to Fray Marcos de Niza on a journey that had nearly proved fatal to Alvar Núñez Cabeza de Vaca and his associates.

Anything might happen.

Fray Marcos de Niza, too, knew all this. Yet he had shown no hesitancy or fear when the proposition was put before him. Rather, he had expressed his eager assent.

Now he was about to set forth on the long and hazardous quest of the seven mysterious cities lying far to the northward.

DON FRANCISCO VÁSQUEZ DE CORONADO, governor of Nueva Galicia, in the province of Nueva España, handed his guest, Fray Marcos de Niza, a sealed letter. It contained the instructions of the noble viceroy, Don Antonio de Mendoza, to the man chosen to represent the Crown in the expedition sent out to find the seven cities.

A little less than thirty years old, a brilliant and fascinating career beckoned to Don Francisco. This hour seemed to signalize its advent.

As the handsome young don scrutinized the face of the friar carefully, noting every characteristic it revealed, he was conscious that this meeting was fraught with momentous consequences for both men.

Beneath a low forehead fringed by curling locks of black hair, the deep-set eyes of Fray Marcos burned like twin lamps in their sockets. Looking out from an oval, olive-tinted face framed by a close-clipped beard, their expression betrayed eager anticipation and yearning, the wistfulness of a sensitive beauty-loving soul.

Fray Marcos de Niza was clothed in the coarse gray robe and white cordelier of his Order, with a rosary of metal and wood depending from the waist. A cloak fashioned of the same material as the robe hung loosely about his slender shoulders, brushing his feet, which were bare save for sandaled shoes of thick hempen cord.

Don Francisco knew that this experienced religious would do everything in his power to fulfill Mendoza's directions. Fray Marcos' reputation for virtue and accomplishment left nothing to be desired.

At the viceroy's table the young man had often heard repeated the weird story told by Alvar Núñez Cabeza de Vaca. Like Mendoza, he retained a lively impression of the sufferings endured by the four salvaged derelicts, and even more, of their reference to seven cities, supposedly teeming with precious treasure. Both Mendoza and Coronado had heard rumors of the existence of these cities long before the appearance of Alvar Núñez in Mexico, but the presence of that unusual man and his relation of his wanderings had kindled to fever pitch in both friends the desire to find and take possession of them.

However, Don Francisco was not unmindful of the difficulties and perils which must be encountered by this gentle-souled friar in the accomplishment of his task.

Might it not happen that he, also, would be taken into slavery by hostile Indians, through whose territory he must pass on the way to the magical cities? In the horrid wastes of desert and amid the treacherous mountain passes, might not the problem of finding food and water become extremely serious? These, and other disagreeable possibilities filtered through Don Francisco's mind as he waited for Fray Marcos to finish the reading of Mendoza's orders. He would have experienced no little chagrin had he known that the viceroy directed the friar to examine into and give an account of the young governor's administration of the affairs of Nueva Galicia.

Provided by his host with the requisites for writing, Fray Marcos applied himself to compose an acknowledgment of the viceroy's paper. When this was completed, he handed the statement to Coronado.

It was as follows:

"I, Fray Marcos de Niza, of the Order of Saint Francis, declare that I received a copy of these instructions, signed by the most illustrious lord, Don Antonio de Mendoza, viceroy and governor of Nueva España, which was delivered to me by command of his lordship and in his name, by Francisco Vásquez de Coronado, governor of this Nueva Galicia. The said copy is taken from these instructions, *de verbo ad verbum,* corrected by them, and made to agree with them. I promise faithfully to fulfill the said instructions and not to go against them or to exceed them in anything therein contained, now or at any time. And as I will thus adhere to and fulfill them, I sign hereto my name at Tonala, on the twentieth day of November, in the year one thousand five hundred and thirty-eight, where was given and delivered to me in the said name the said instructions, and which is in the province of Nueva Galicia."

Don Francisco approved the statement and hastened to assure Fray Marcos that everything possible would be done to assure him a safe and successful journey.

"You will find my Indians of great service, Father," he said. "They are well trained in the Spanish language and they know most of the native dialects. However, your best ally will be the Moor, Estevan. This slave traveled over a great part of the country to the north with Dorantes, his master, and the others. He is so valuable, in fact, that Dorantes would not sell him, even to the viceroy, for any amount of money. Upon fervent persuasions, he finally consented to lease him to Don Antonio in order that he might go on this journey of reconnaissance. I have no doubt but that this Moor will serve you faithfully. Should it happen otherwise, severe punishment will be meted out to him."

Fray Marcos, listening attentively, bowed his head in assent.

As they talked further, the young hidalgo looked closely at the robe of the friar, worn, and patched in several places. He knew that its condition was a badge of honor in the service of Lady Poverty. The governor highly respected the religious orders of the Church, as did every good Spaniard, but he had no wish to be poor.

His eyes strayed to the crudely fashioned sandals on Fray Marcos' feet . . . he wondered how far they would serve the man of God when the road led over stones and through brambles. Then, too, the partly exposed feet would afford an excellent target for a poisoned arrow!

Estevan the Moor had shown himself to be a greedy, ambitious man. Was it possible that he might fall from his position of trust and responsibility and stoop to betray his superior, when far from the viceroy's reach? What then?

Coronado chose to think that God and our Lady, with the glorious Seraph of Assisi, Saint Francis, would protect their spiritual son and bring him safely through all perils and difficulties. And, when he should return to Mexico with glorious news for the viceroy, then someone else would set forth to reap a harvest of honor and emolument in those countries which Fray Marcos should discover.

The governor's brilliant eyes rested on a representation of his family coat of arms hanging on the opposite wall. On one side his forbears were descended from the royal blood of France. Emblazoned on their escutcheon were three silver fleurs-de-lis in a field of azure. The Spanish branch of the family, the Vásquez, had as their emblem a rampant golden lion wearing a gold crown, set forth on a crimson field and embroidered with eight blue fleurs-de-lis.

The only emblems Fray Marcos claimed were his well-worn robe and cord and our Lady's rosary.

Don Francisco was well satisfied for the present with his worldly estate and judged that by the holiness and valor of the friar who sat beside him he soon might attain to a great prize.

Born at Salamanca in 1510, the future conquistador had grown into young manhood at a time when Spain was extending her dominions to become the most extensive realm the world seemed destined to know. In the Church his family name was illustrious — but Francisco was not for the Church. Sent to court, he had met Mendoza and soon afterward accompanied him to the colonies of the New World. Here for a time he had worked side by side with the viceroy as his personal secretary. Married to the daughter of a deceased royal treasurer of Spain, wealthy in her own right, Don Francisco judged his lot to be far from unpleasant. Thinking now of his beloved wife, he said to Fray Marcos:

"As you know, Father, our noble viceroy is keenly desirous of having all his followers happily married. In the granting of lands married men have always been given preference over single men. However, I can assure you that this fact had no bearing on my choice of Doña Beatriz d'Estrada for my wife. Not her high position and extensive properties, but the beauty of her character, which complements that of her countenance and form, influenced me in the matter."

Fray Marcos de Niza could realize that the union of Coronado and his lady was truly a love match — the light in the young man's eyes as he spoke her name revealed that fact. The friar wondered if, perchance, this great devotion might not prove an obstacle to the career of one who aspired to the lofty role of conquistador. For a man deeply in love is unhappy when long absent from the object of his affections. One day Coronado's soldiers were to complain bitterly of this devotion, which they would deem in some measure responsible for the apparent failure of a great undertaking.

Fray Marcos de Niza replaced in the folds of his robe the paper containing Mendoza's instructions. His heart was aglow with quiet happiness as he thought of the souls of poor pagans whose salvation might be assured by means of this enterprise.

But Don Francisco Vásquez de Coronado was thinking of something else. His mind reverted to a gold ornament, found by the company of the one-eyed Narváez, in their search through a deserted village on an island off the bay of Florida. Surely, there was more of the precious metal in places beyond — more, and to be had for the taking!

In the meantime, Alvar Núñez Cabeza de Vaca had gone to Spain, to prosecute at the royal court his plans for future undertakings. For the present, at least, his wanderings in the New World were at an end. But he had kindled a spark in the breasts of his illustrious countrymen which was growing rapidly into a mighty sweeping flame.

The noble governor of Nueva Galicia was grateful to Alvar Núñez and his companions for having provided an incentive to the fondest ambition his life had entertained thus far.

OVER dreary and monotonous plains that seemed to the marchers endless, Governor Coronado, Fray Marcos de Niza, Estevan and the other members of this picturesque company passed on their way to San Miguel de Culiacán on the western coast of Sinaloa, Mexico. When two rivers, the Piaxtla and the Elota, had been safely crossed, they drew near to the limits of Nueva Galicia.

Their goal, the little border town of San Miguel de Culiacán, had been founded by the young Don Núño de Guzmán, who set out from Mexico City in 1529 on a tour of exploration. Highly successful as a conquistador, Guzmán had proved himself most cruel and rapacious in his treatment of the Indians.

"Guzmán conquered Jalisco and Sinaloa [in western Mexico] in just two years' time," the governor explained. "In Jalisco he founded the towns of Compostela and Guadalajara, and in Sinaloa those of San Miguel de Culiacán and Chiametla. You are probably not familiar with this terrain, Father. . . . Like Cortés, Guzmán became presumptuous and so incurred the displeasure of the Crown. The name he bestowed on the newly conquered territory, 'Greater Spain,' was promptly changed by the authorities to Nueva Galicia."

Fray Marcos eagerly questioned whether it was not true that the reports of seven very important cities lying

to the north had originated with Guzmán. The governor
replied:

"I believe the tale originated with one of Guzmán's
Indians, whom our people called Tejo.

"This boy's father, a trader, was accustomed to travel
into the back country with a stock of feathers and other
ornaments dear to the hearts of the natives. There he
would exchange them for gold and silver. A great quantity of both metals was said to exist in those parts. Upon
returning home, the trader never failed to extol the riches
of the place he had visited. Later, Tejo himself accompanied his father on several of his excursions, and the boy
stated that during the journey he had seen a number of
large villages, resembling Mexico. There were seven of
these villages, Tejo affirmed, and they were exceptionally
large and rich; silversmiths plied their trade in the streets,
and wonderful were the products resulting from their
skillful work."

In answer to Fray Marcos' question as to how far north
these cities were supposed to be located, Coronado
replied:

"To reach them from Tejo's home required forty days
of journeying. On the way one passed through a wilderness which boasted no vegetation except some plants
about a span in height.

"Naturally, Núño de Guzmán, then president of the
Audencia" [the administrative and judicial board of
Nueva Espana] "was moved to the quick by the Indian
boy's story. He accepted it as truth, and as soon as possible he collected a company of nearly four hundred
Spaniards and twenty thousand Indians. With these he
set out to find the seven cities.

"Northward, along the coast of the South Sea [the
Pacific] they proceeded until they reached an Indian
village called Ciguatan. At this place they heard of Culia-

cán. They advanced to find it, and some of Guzmán's men finally reached the Mayo River, on the borders of Sinaloa and Sonora. This was in 1530. One year later a small settlement was made at Culiacán, in Sinaloa. From this station the white men carried on their infamous slave trade, visiting southern Sonora for the purpose of ensnaring Indian victims."

Fray Marcos inquired about the present relations between the Spaniards of San Miguel de Culiacán and the natives. Coronado frowned darkly as he answered:

"Unfortunately, they have not been the best. White men are feared and disliked by the Indians because the latter have been treated so badly by our people. The Spaniards have forced the natives to work for them, because they themselves are too lazy to cultivate their crops. Due to this state of things, many of the Indians have left the place and are at present hiding in the mountains. As you know, our noble viceroy is very anxious to remedy this situation."

Coronado here mentioned the name of a man of whom the friar had already heard. This was Melchior Díaz, a soldier who enjoyed an enviable reputation for lofty character and achievement.

"After the conquest," he said, "Guzmán placed a brilliant and able official, Melchior Díaz, in charge of the territory. While not of noble ancestry, Díaz gained great prestige because of his dependability and skill. He is a determined worker, and an able organizer and leader. You will meet him shortly. One of the few good things Núño de Guzmán did was to entrust the care of the newly acquired country to him."

As they neared the town, the young Don issued orders to his captains and soldiers.

"I do not wish to cause inconvenience to the townspeople," he announced. "Therefore, I shall not ask

quarters for you in the town. We shall camp on the out-
skirts, at least for the time being."

The governor was overjoyed to find that his consideration for the comfort of his countrymen in the town evoked
a warm response from these people. They invited every
officer of rank to partake of the hospitality of their homes,
and even urged many to reside with them during their
stay.

When, a little later, the townspeople and soldiers were
gathered in the plaza, Fray Marcos de Niza, in com-
pliance with the viceroy's orders, addressed them.

The friar explained that he was commissioned to com-
municate to them the regulations of the viceroy. These
were that the Indians who were disposed to be friendly
must be treated with the utmost consideration. They
were not to be employed in exhausting labors or
given burdens so difficult to bear that their health and
spirits would be injured thereby. Fray Marcos assured
them that strict obedience to the orders would merit
favor with His Majesty, who was always disposed to reward well the services of his good and true subjects. On
his part, the viceroy had promised that he would be
prompt to set forth their claims to the reward promised
them by the Crown.

If, on the contrary, any of the Spaniards were to act
against these orders, swift punishment would be meted
out to them, as to all disloyal men.

The townspeople and soldiers listened respectfully to
the friar's address. However, watching them intently, Don
Francisco was not at all certain that the orders would be
fully carried out. The Indians of San Miguel de Culiacán
were highly useful to the Spaniards, and it was not prob-
able that the latter would relinquish willingly their
previous customs when to do so would cause them serious
inconvenience.

Lastly, Fray Marcos de Niza addressed himself to the Indians, who were lined up at the sides in the rear of the assembly.

"In the name of His Majesty the King," he began, "I come to give you assurance that you will be well treated in the future, although you have suffered much in the past from white men. His Majesty the King is deeply grieved that this is so. He wishes me to tell you that from henceforth you shall be treated honorably, and any who harm you must suffer the punishment of their misdeeds.

"From this time forward there shall be no more slaves among you, nor shall you be driven from your lands. But you shall be free on them, without hurt or damage. So, put away fear and recognize God, our Lord, who is in heaven, and the Emperor, who is placed on earth by His hand to rule and govern it."

Coronado, continuing to observe Fray Marcos attentively, could not but admire the serenity of the friar's aspect, as well as the calm fearlessness of his words. For once in his life, the young Don found it a little embarrassing to sit on horseback while this distinguished son of Saint Francis trudged humbly on foot beside him. He understood the spirit of the religious, and he marveled at it. Saint Francis was a wise and temperate ruler, he thought. He did not forbid his sons to ride if they were afflicted with any infirmity. If the great heart of the Saint of Assisi was compassionate even toward the dumb creatures of the universe, how much more toward his own beloved subjects. In Fray Marcos the young governor beheld the mirror of a true Franciscan, so that he could readily grasp the philosophy of him who was called the Seraphic Patriarch. When, for instance, the friar partook of the ordinary meals along the route, he ate in all simplicity what was set before him, making no distinction of viands. And it seemed that the man of God was never idle, being always occupied either in prayer, in teaching the Indians to make the Sign of the Cross, or in otherwise showing an amiable and intelligent interest in his associates.

From Fray Marcos Coronado's glance shifted to a lone figure standing behind the Indians, at the rear of the plaza. It was that of Estevan the Moor. To the hidalgo of Spain the presence of this black man, who bore an expression of strange cunning and licentiousness written in his features, became repulsive in the extreme. Did Fray Marcos de Niza, also, find it so? The friar was gentle by nature, wholly devoted to God and to the Church. Poverty and humility were the watchwords of the great religious organization to which he belonged. Its Founder had indicated no less when he wrote in his rules:

"And I counsel admonish and exhort my friars, in the Lord Jesus, that when they go through the world they neither quarrel nor contend in words, nor judge others, but let them be gentle, peaceful and modest, meek and humble, speaking uprightly to all as becometh. . . ."

There could be no greater contrast than that which existed between the renowned son of the Poverello of Assisi and the Moorish slave, whose unique experiences in his wanderings with his Spanish masters had prepared him for anything. Unfortunately, Estevan was the only man who could serve Fray Marcos usefully in his dealings with the native tribes. The Moor's past history had furnished him with knowledge most valuable for the attainment of Viceroy Mendoza's end, and his talents as interpreter were not to be despised. But to the genuine, straightforward Don Francisco Vásquez de Coronado, he was disagreeable in the extreme, his grossly swollen lips, the result of overindulgence in chili peppers, giving evidence of his sensual nature. He knew much that the governor would like to know, and it was galling to Coro-

nado that Estevan would tell no more about himself than
he chose to tell. Even then it was impossible to distinguish between truth and fiction, since his recital invariably was embellished with many compliments to himself as the real leader of a tragic odyssey of eight terrible
years.

Coronado knew that Estevan believed himself to be
much better than the white men. For what did it profit
the Spaniards to ride fine horses and wear glittering
armor; to possess princely figures and comely countenances, in a land whose inhabitants were rude uncultivated savages, pagans who worshiped the elements and
who, to greater or less extent, were hostile to any influence which was alien to themselves?

Estevan's unbridled appetite for food was equaled only
by his gluttony for admiration. Sometimes, by making use
of the most adroit expressions in the native dialects,
sometimes by the expert use of the symbols of the sign
language, he succeeded in inspiring in most of the Indians a sense of veneration and awe. At first they had
tried to remove the black from the Moor's face, scraping
it with their fingers in the belief that it would come off.
Estevan had laughed at this, assuring them that this was
one kind of paint that stayed on. . . . A great skulking
fellow with a heavy mass of tangled black hair, he was
ever on the lookout for occasions of profit or satisfaction
to himself.

Coronado's meditation was terminated abruptly by
the return of Fray Marcos to his side. Dismounting from
his horse and removing his helmet, he addressed the friar:

"Father, I wish you a safe and prosperous journey with
Fray Onorato and our good Indians. The blessing of God
upon your adventure! May you soon return with the best
possible news for us. As I said previously, you can trust
your native guides implicitly. They are Nebomes, a

branch of the Pima family. You may know that they were with Alvar Núñez Cabeza de Vaca for a time. Later, they settled down at Bamoa, on the Rio Petatlán. Don Antonio de Mendoza had them sent to Mexico and there trained as linguists. I do not think you need fear a poor reception from the tribes to the north if you send these Indians on before you, to reassure the others of your friendly intentions. I have found that usually the natives are peaceable if one does not molest them and if they think our intentions toward them are honest. Remember always, Father, you are the leader of this little company and have the right to exact perfect obedience from all your followers."

Fray Marcos thanked the young don as he replied, graciously:

"For the service of our Lord!"

GOVERNOR CORONADO had taken the precaution of sending six of his own Indians ahead of Fray Marcos and his escort to assure the native tribes to the north of what he had expressed as "the honest intentions" of the friar and his companions. Because of this wise move a safe and peaceful journey was assured the little company.

The region into which they penetrated after leaving San Miguel de Culiacán was for the most part uninhabited. It was an arid, sterile country, whose roads were the worst possible. Núño de Guzmán, the first white man to set forth in search of the seven cities, had experienced these difficulties and eventually had given up the quest. Now, two Franciscan friars, their Moorish guide, and a band of brown men traveled on their way to accomplish, if possible, what Guzmán had failed to achieve.

Fray Marcos rejoiced in the prospect before him, even though fully aware that his goal would not be attained without difficulties and perils of every kind. The remembrance of the poor pagans who might be won to the faith of Jesus Christ steeled his resolution to conquer all obstacles. His lips moved in prayer as he walked beside his one white companion, Fray Onorato, a simple trusting soul, whose companionship afforded his brother religious no small happiness and consolation. Fray Onorato would be of service in many ways, not the least important of

37

which was serving Fray Marcos at the Holy Sacrifice of the Mass when circumstances permitted the friars to enjoy this greatest of all boons. Also, the brother could instruct the natives in the Sign of the Cross and acquaint them, through the interpreters, with a few fundamental truths of the Christian religion.

Estevan the Moor, as a Christian convert, might help in this task — but Fray Marcos placed little reliance on the good will of Estevan or the integrity of his motives. Time would reveal how far he could be trusted to fulfill even the important duty to which Viceroy Mendoza had assigned him.

"See, Brother! There is a settlement ahead!" Fray Marcos suddenly cried out, as, from the wastes of sand in the distance the outline of a straggling native village emerged.

Coming up to it, the friars found that it was a cluster of small round dwellings whose doors were set so low that a man must stoop to enter them.

As the inhabitants came out to stare in surprise at the white men, Fray Marcos greeted them with a friendly smile and made the Sign of the Cross over them. They repeated the act, although imperfectly, after him, with every indication of respect and approval.

Estevan, who stood by, remarked that the Indians did not connect the sacred symbol with the religion of the white men; to them it was an emblem of their deities, the sun and moon.

As the travelers proceeded on their way, passing through other similar hamlets, they found that the Indians of this region raised corn, but only a small supply of it, for the soil was sandy and, therefore, unfavorable for agriculture. They also cultivated beans and melons, and provided themselves with a little game, consisting of rabbits, hare, and deer.

As the brother returned from a short trip of inspection, Fray Marcos asked him whether he had found any evidence of human sacrifices.

Fray Onorato replied in the negative — he had discovered no trace of any sacrifices.

The Indians were friendly, and very inquisitive. They tagged after the friars, as well as after Estevan the Moor, who seemed to be an object of great attraction to them because of his black skin. The men wore no clothing, but the women were clothed in a garment of tanned white deerskin, covering them from the waist to the feet, and resembling a skirt.

The friars had need of stout courage, not so much to protect themselves from the war implements of this primitive people, which consisted of poisoned arrows, spears and obsidian-edged swords, as from the strange unattractive comrades they discovered on entering the huts to partake of the hospitality of the inmates. Thus, in one instance, a large sinister-appearing snake reared its ugly head in a dim corner, and a moment later glided across the floor to the entrance of the small habitation, passing at the very feet of the men of God.

Thrusting his head into the hut, Estevan explained:

"These people think it an honor to keep reptiles in their homes and to pay them veneration."

Other comrades less obnoxious to the white men, domesticated birds, came to pay their respects, especially turkeys, which entered the huts to strut about the friars in lordly fashion.

Idol worship, the visitors discovered, was general among the natives of Culiacán. This, with the many indecent representations painted on the inner walls of the houses, was a source of disgust to the pure-souled religious.

As they continued on their way the little band came to

a settlement in which the Indians were observing market day. In the center of the village men were haggling over the price of their prospective wives. This, however, seemed a matter of indifference to the native maidens, who, without any excitement, awaited the outcome of the business. When all was concluded, the men drank copiously of a beverage prepared from the pitahaya fruit or mesquite beans, or in some cases from agave, honey, and wheat. How woefully intoxicating this drink could be the friars had reason to know from observing the behavior of the men who freely partook of it.

These natives, like all the tribes of northern Mexico, subsisted chiefly on wild fruits; the pitahaya, honey, grain, roots, fish, and larvae. They captured game, large and small, for food. Some ate rats, mice, snakes, and vermin. Fray Onorato, whose health was not robust, sickened at their revolting practices, but Fray Marcos de Niza did not appear to notice such things. His many and varied experiences in Santo Domingo and Peru had accustomed him to meet distasteful sights without being affected by them.

"You remember, Brother, how the temptation to lead a solitary life in prayer and penance strongly drew our Blessed Father Francis," Fray Marcos said in gentle tone to Brother Onorato. "He loved the quiet valley in the Sabine hills, where nature alone, after God, spoke to him. But he relinquished the attraction after seeking and obtaining the divine guidance. He elected to live the active life, combined with the life of prayer, and so he went forth into difficult places to save souls from the wiles of the evil one and win them to their Creator. We are in a good way, Brother. Let us be intent on high things and go on in peace together."

The mornings were cold in Culiacán and, in consequence, refreshing. Fray Marcos thankfully accepted the use of little shelters put up for him by the natives, who wove together roots and palms to provide a roof of thatch over his head. Even so, he found his bones and muscles stiff and sore when he awoke in the crisp red dawn, after a sound night's sleep — for the march, so far uninterrupted by a single day, induced extreme weariness.

The friar did not find the native dialects spoken in the province of Culiacán embarrassing to any extent. The Pima Indians of his escort could manage most of them. Others of these dialects were familiar to Estevan, or else the Moor employed the Indian sign language to good effect. One annoyance Fray Marcos did suffer in this exigency — he never could rest sure that the black man would continue faithful in his allegiance. This was a trial from which there was no escaping.

Each of the three chief tribes of Culiacán spoke a distinctive language. These tribes were the Tahues, the Pacaxees and the Acaxees. Among them, the Tahues were the best and most intelligent; they were stable in their habits and inclined to be friendly to strangers.

The second group, the Pacaxees, made their habitations between the plains and the mountains. They were far less civilized than the Tahues. People of this tribe, who dwelt in the higher altitudes, ate the flesh of human beings and had other customs that were degraded and revolting. A Pacaxee might have as many wives as he chose. His deities were embodied in certain stones, which he carved and painted in grotesque designs. Witchcraft and sorcery were dear to his heart.

The third tribe, the Acaxees, had their little villages ranged along the hills and in the mountains. They possessed most of this terrain. When they went hunting they were as likely to be scouting for men as for beasts. They habitually ate human flesh. Living in tiny settlements and in a country exceedingly rough and unpleasant, they never descended to the plains or mingled with other tribes. Their territory was cut across by numerous small ravines. These depressions, seemingly innocent, were in reality treacherous and impassable. Indians from the different settlements could speak to one another across them, but might not pass over them. Small provocation sufficed for members of the two latter groups to set upon and eat one another.

The Acaxees were diligent observers of the heavenly bodies, yet so depraved that, in addition to other vicious customs, they decorated their dwellings with horrid and revolting pictures.

One of the Pimas in the friars' escort explained the meaning of certain small sticks that were found planted in the soil.

"They are jiote sticks, cut from the turpentine tree," he said, "and are superstitious devices. The principal intermediaries of these Indians, and the ministers of their idols, are the wizards. The Acaxees also offer food to supposedly supernatural beings, and make use of shamanistic methods of curing their sick."

"Only six years ago Núño de Guzmán sent an expedition into this rude valley," Fray Marcos observed to Fray Onorato. "It was organized in this spot, and afterward marched to the Rio Petatlán, where we are now going. After they reached this river, they pressed on through Sinaloa and the Rio Fuerte to the Rio Mayo and the Yaqui Valley. The latter stage of their journey was made over a road lined with rocks and extremely difficult to traverse. The party suffered greatly from lack of water, especially on the final day of the march. The best they could do was to break open the great cacti that lined the way and suck the liquid from the stems."

Fray Onorato paled slightly as his brother friar thus intimated what lay ahead. Already the good lay brother was showing signs of physical depression as a result of the march. The change was shrewdly observed by his companion. The prospect of losing his one white associate on the way to the seven cities was not a consoling one to Fray Marcos, but he dared to hope for the best. Yet he, too, had reminiscences of a different world that he had freely left behind him for the love of Christ.

Looking across the plains, he saw that the hills for many miles were etched sharply against the brightness of the sky. Soon the descending sun would shed a glory over them. It recalled to him his native Savoy, when at evening the same sun gilded the olive-clad slopes and corn fields and the radiant gardens where roses, carnations and mignonette vied with each other in regal splendor.

Far away — but the vision was enshrined deeply in his heart! Above was the vast amphitheater of mountains, rising beyond his native Nice; below, the Mediterranean mirrored in its shining surface villas and terraces, avenues of stately pines and cypresses, and the white roads winding into the sunset.

An itinerant musician, with a row of bells on his forehead and Pandean pipes at his lips, was toiling up the hill beneath a monastery gate. His shoulders were stooped and weary after a hard day spent in making music for the world. In the shelter of a clump of magnolias children were running in and out between the lustrous foliage where conelike pods showed bright vermilion-colored seeds. Along the monastery wall a lantana plant trailed its red and yellow blossoms, and the fragrance of almond flowers hung rich in the air.

There were the olive groves and cornfields which, some said, the Greeks had planted there over two thousand years ago; and there, too, was the cemetery of the town, with its stigmatized Saint, the Seraph of Assisi, leaning down in effigy over the gate.

In the belfry of the monastery the huge bell was ringing. . . .

Fray Marcos de Niza stretched out his hand as if to caress like a friend the lantana plant.

It was not there.

He opened his eyes.

Gone was the vision. In its place was a mean little Indian village in Culiacán, with its prayer sticks waving in the winds, wild birds searching for food in the soil, and natives standing at the doors of their miserable huts, or walking by him with that ever inscrutable expression, that no white man could comprehend, on their stolid faces.

At that moment Fray Marcos de Niza forgot all about his important mission, the hopes and fears, the joys and sorrows that lay ahead on the trail. His gray robe, with the white cordelier at the waist, and his cloak, protecting his frail body from the chill winds, reminded him of something greater than all earthly things, and his spirit found rest in God, who was present to him alike in Culiacán and Nice.

CONTINUING for twenty leagues northward, veering slightly to the west, Fray Marcos de Niza and his party came to a little settlement of houses whose roofs, thatched with petates, or grass mats, gave the place its name, Petatlán. Some few of the dwellings were constructed of adobe, but the majority were of cane and palm leaves. Through this verdant terrain ran a pleasant river, the Rio Petatlán.

Estevan informed his chief that houses similar to these were to be found for more than two hundred leagues ahead, as far as the beginning of the region where the seven cities supposedly were located. The Sonora Valley, which must be crossed first, lay one hundred and thirty leagues beyond. Between Petatlán and Sonora there were several rivers, so that a fair water supply was assured the travelers.

The natives of Petatlán cultivated some maize; also squash and melons from seed left by the Spaniard, Alcarez, and his party when they passed this way. They also raised beans and cotton.

As in Culiacán, while the temperature in the village was fairly low in the early part of the day, with the ascent of the sun it rapidly grew warmer until by midafternoon the heat was fairly intense. During this part of the day the two friars kept the hood of their robe drawn over their heads as protection from the sun's brilliant rays.

Fray Marcos and Onorato were accustomed to a different climate — in Mexico City the entire day was cool and invigorating.

The Indians dwelling in the country of Petatlán were Cáhitas. They employed a language different from that of the Tahues, yet both groups could understand one another's speech without much difficulty.

Spanish slavers and traders, making their headquarters in Culiacán, had brought great misery upon these harmless natives. Now, seeing white men entering their domain, they hastened forward and offered them lodging and food. Fear, rather than courtesy, dictated their action. They had no reason to think that the newcomers were different from those of the white race who had previously visited them. Even the friendly assurances of the Pimas in the friar's company could not dissipate this distrust.

The Indian men of Petatlán wore scant clothing. The women, however, were clothed in dresses heavily embroidered with some sort of gems. Ornaments, adroitly fashioned, hung from their ears. Since the Cáhitas possessed no instrument for piercing the jewel, they were accustomed to cut a small groove around it and so string it together with others of its kind. They made necklaces and bracelets, also, and were exceptionally skillful in working jewels into representations of animals and birds. These figures were afterward sewn on cloth. As the rays of the sun shone upon the finished garments, the effect was dazzling.

Fray Marcos and the lay brother, having partaken of a light repast of beans and pumpkin, washed down by a cool draught of water from the river, sat at the door of the little hut allotted to them and watched the sun slowly receding from the maize fields. The priest opened a little parcel he had taken from his pocket and in a few moments was engaged in mending a torn place in his robe.

The air was moist and somewhat warm, and Fray Marcos noted how pale and listless his companion appeared to be.

Just then, behind the distant coastal hills bordering the Sinaloa country, the sun was descending in a bank of vermilion-colored clouds. Its rays spattered the earth for miles around, covering the hills and fields with glory.

"It is like the halo about the head of the Eternal Father," observed Fray Marcos, as he pointed to the horizon with his disengaged hand. "From every one of those darts of light, grace might well be descending upon the earth."

Their toil in the fields ended for the day, some of the Indians were playing a game of ball. Their lithe brown bodies, leaping and descending in the sunset glow, formed a picture of perfect symmetry and grace. The utmost agility was required in the exercise of this sport, since the ball might never be permitted to touch the earth.

At a little distance another group of natives were fashioning bunches of bright-colored feathers to their shields.

In the meantime, Estevan the Moor was enjoying his own peculiar pastime. Squatting by the river's bank, he was regaling his company with a braggart account of feats which he asserted he had performed. Tremendous lies, of course, as Fray Marcos de Niza, watching him, could well imagine. This, however, was far from being the most serious of his offenses. His superior found numerous occasions for reprimanding him, but he did not do so harshly, recognizing the necessity for keeping the Moor in good humor.

Just now a different kind of trial was close ahead for Fray Marcos. His friar companion, Fray Onorato, realized that his frail strength was unequal to the test near at hand. He was loath to admit to his father and friend that the strain of the journey had by this time taxed his physical resources to the breaking point.

Excusing himself, he entered the hut and stretched himself on his bed of palm leaves, while Fray Marcos remained outside, watching the light fading from the serrated spurs to westward. A low moan issuing from the hut quickly brought him to his feet. When he reached Onorato's side, he found that the good brother was flushed with fever and his lips were parched.

Fray Marcos employed such simple remedies as he had at hand, and soon the sick man had fallen into a fitful slumber, with his priestly brother in religion seated on the floor of the hut to watch by his side.

To the experienced eye of Fray Marcos it was evident that Onorato was unequal to the long difficult journey lying ahead. His peaceful life in the monastery of Jalisco had not inured him to feats of great physical endurance. Clearly, his role in the momentous adventure had come abruptly to an end.

With Onorato left behind in the little settlement of the grass mats, the gallant leader of the party — now its only white man — was not too certain of his future peace of mind. Estevan and the Pima Indians of his party were Christians, true, but they were of other races than his own, and could hardly be expected to receive his confidences. A little fear smote his heart — as if one of the bright darts of light he had watched falling aslant on the mountains had struck into his soul and mortally wounded him.

What to do in this fierce trial of doubt and distrust?

The faithful son of Saint Francis of Assisi knew what to do.

His fingers sought the beads hanging at his side. He drew them toward his lips and kissed the image of the Crucified One, tenderly. Then he began the recitation of the prayer greatly endeared to every member of his Order — the Franciscan Crown.

He asked help from our Lord, our Lady, Saint Francis, and a little boy of his Order who, over a century before, had been granted a heavenly favor. Now, as Fray Marcos de Niza repeated the Aves for the sick brother and for his own needs, peace came like a gentle dove and settled in the lonely places of his heart.

It did not enter into his mind to send to Don Antonio de Mendoza for anyone to replace Onorato. The noble viceroy had not chosen a weakling to carry out his ambitious designs. Not cowardice, but obedience, humility and abnegation dictated the friar's every act. Knowing this from the testimonials he had received concerning Fray Marcos, Mendoza had been emphatic in ordering him to have a care for his life, and not to expose it needlessly to danger.

Kneeling by Fray Onorato's poor bed of leaves, Marcos de Niza talked to his God as a brave soldier talks to his commander in chief.

When he had finished his devotions he rose from his knees and went out into the soft Mexican night.

In the sky the stars glittered like the jewels the women of Petatlán wore on their garments. The river prayed as it slipped on its way to join the South Sea.

Here, where thickly crowded settlements extended from mountains to sea, holding so many souls ignorant of the true God and their eternal destiny, most abominable vices prevailed. Here, then, men must be brought to the knowledge and the love and the service of the one true God. . . .

Fray Marcos was not, however, to linger at Petatlán to instruct and baptize the Indians. His was not now the role of missionary, but of herald and pioneer. He must blaze a trail across desert and mesa, mountain and valley over which, one day, missionaries would toil to reach these needy ones.

Advancing to the river's bank, Fray Marcos stooped and bathed his hands and face. Then he sat down among the long cool reeds and, removing his sandals, dipped his feet into the stream. When he had dried them with handfuls of grass, he returned to the hut and knelt down beside his mattress of palm to make his evening prayer.

VII

REGRETFULLY Fray Marcos de Niza bade farewell to Fray Onorato, once more falling back, not on his own thought, but on the consoling words of their holy father, Saint Francis:

"O, dearly beloved and eternally blessed children, hear me, hear the voice of your Father. Great things have we promised, still greater are promised to us. Let us keep the former, let us strive for the latter. Pleasure is short, punishment eternal. Suffering is small, glory without measure. Many are called, few are chosen; to all shall retribution be made. Amen."

Humbly resigned to forego the great happiness he had anticipated, that of accompanying his beloved superior on the northward journey, Fray Onorato thankfully received the blessing of his brother religious. And so, with the promise of faithful prayers for one another, the two men parted.

From his leafy couch the sick brother watched the lithe figure of Fray Marcos, as, stooping low, he passed through the entrance to the hut and out into the green valley.

"Suffering is small" — Onorato whispered the words to himself, that he might assimilate their full import. And, after them, those other words that contained so rich a promise: "glory without measure."

Would Fray Marcos reap in this present world the reward of the heroic service he had elected to give in the interests of God and country? Fray Onorato wondered about that. Saint Francis had not promised his loyal sons satisfaction in this life, but only in the life to come.

In his youth Onorato had experienced all the heart-warming joys to which Fray Marcos, also, was accustomed. The brother, too, could visualize the rose-girt hills and verdant groves of a cherished homeland. It was not difficult for him to transport himself to that familiar spot and in spirit to participate in the innocent carefree pleasures of former days. . . . Again he was at play with other boys of his age, beside a fountain made of stones and glass. Its shining swans, fashioned of cockleshells, preened themselves in the sunlight. Above, tall carouba and pin parasol trees retained their verdure all the year, keeping their freshness and beauty long after the withered foliage of other trees had floated to the earth. . . .

When the sick brother opened his eyes, the vision was gone, but his mind still followed and his prayer accompanied the soldierlike figure of his revered friend, passing along by the river's bank.

As he proceeded through the settlement, Fray Marcos de Niza was pleased to see the natives of the various villages hastening to greet him. They had learned of the approach of a white man and were eager to converse with him and his followers. Some of these natives were nomads, whose habitations were in the thickets of the woods along the seashore and sand dunes. At the time of harvest, these Indians were accustomed to visit the villages of friendly agriculturists in order to purchase provisions.

The Indians of Sinaloa, the country of Fray Marcos' present journeying, remembered the "Medicine Man," Alvar Núñez Cabeza de Vaca, who had "cured" their sick by placing his hands upon them and praying over them. When first they heard of the coming of Fray Marcos, they had hastened to set up little leafy bowers for his reception, twining flowers into the foliage, and had prepared gifts for him.

The friar knew that the natives credited Alvar Núñez with supernatural powers, whereas the Christian-minded explorer had acted only that he might win their trust and friendship, and had placed no reliance whatsoever on his own powers. In His goodness, God had deigned to grant the fulfillment of his prayer, as it seemed, for many of the sick Indians had recovered their health.

Fray Marcos taught his new acquaintances how to make the Sign of the Cross, and, through the interpreters, explained its meaning to them. Men and women repeated the act after him, with greater or less success. No further instruction could be given them, for the friar knew that he must press on and leave to other missionaries, who should follow in his footsteps, the task of teaching and baptizing.

Greatly refreshed by their three days' sojourn at Petatlán, Fray Marcos and his caravan tramped along at a lively pace. Soon they were passing through an uninhabited stretch of country on the lower Rio Petatlán, a coastal region. As they proceeded, they observed that the landscape became completely altered. Trees ceased to appear, unless for an occasional gaunt pine, lifting its lonely head into the heavens.

Fruits grew scarce until only the tuna, the thorny mesquite and the pitahaya cactus dotted the dull red soil. The tuna was a prickly pear, the size of an egg, sometimes black, sometimes red in appearance. The mesquite was a shrub of the mimosa family, bearing rich sugar in its pods; its beans, when reduced to meal, made excellent cakes. The pitahaya, a type of pomegranate, was the fruit of a great thistle; from it the Indians made a wine which could befuddle their senses completely.

Fray Marcos was attracted by a giant cactus of the pitahaya species which held its wide-spreading branches across the pathway in seemingly belligerent mood. He noted that at frequent intervals the branches bore sharp pointed spines, several inches in length. Between these spines the fruit gleamed, a deep crimson in color.

Taking out his knife, the friar was about to cut away a specimen of the fruit when one of his Pimas leaped forward and snatched the implement from his hand. The Indian explained that, inexperienced as Fray Marcos was in dealing with the treacherous plant, he would have wounded himself badly on its evil spines, had he performed the operation.

The Pima deftly removed a fine sample of the pitahaya from its branch and presented it to his superior.

Fray Marcos cut it open. Its pulp, of a fine crimson color, contained many seeds, resembling those of a fig. Its flavor proved to be most agreeable. The juice relieved the friar's thirst, and the water carried in long-necked jars by the caravan now seemed insipid by comparison.

Other pitahayas there were, the Pima said, that were yellow in appearance, and contained a white pulp and black seeds. This species was not as useful as the crimson variety, from which a very good ink, either purple or red in color, could be made.

Fray Marcos missed the song of the river in this lonely wilderness of sand and spine. When at night a pale lemon-colored moon scaled majestically above the clouds, like an emperor treading the stairway of his palace, he gathered the Indians of his escort about him and led them in their evening prayers. These finished, he retired to the leafy shelter prepared for him by Estevan the Moor, with the aid of native helpers. Not always, however, did sleep come quickly to sooth his eyelids, strained and sore from the glare of the sun.

The desert through which Fray Marcos was now journeying continued to show little vegetation and scant beauty for the inner refreshment and consolation of the wayfarer. Dreary and changeless, it stretched away, seeming to have no limit, and with never a mirage to gladden the eye and brighten the jaded spirits. Happily Fray Marcos could remember One who had sojourned and fasted forty days in a wilderness before going forward to his mission among men.

"Pilgrims and strangers," Saint Francis had called his friars, men traveling on a brief journey through a land of exile and tears to eternal mansions. For so read his words:

"The friars shall appropriate nothing to themselves, neither a house nor place, nor anything. And as pilgrims and strangers in this world, serving the Lord in poverty and humility . . . poor in goods but exalted in virtue. Let this be your portion, which leads to the land of the living."

"Neither house nor place." Fray Marcos' present mansion was a flimsy bower constructed of sticks and leaves, his "place" an unpromising terrain which must be won for Christ before anything more satisfying should succeed. Courage, confidence and fortitude were needed to accomplish this difficult feat.

"Father, another group of Indians from this country are following us," one the Pimas reported to the friar, absorbed in these contemplations.

"Are they friends?" Fray Marcos inquired.

"They are," was the assurance given.

At this, he ordered that they be brought to him.

A goodly number presented themselves, all bearing supplies of food. They informed him that it was intended for the white man and his followers. They were Sinaloans, and asked to be allowed to remain with the caravan. Fray Marcos gave permission and they retired, well satisfied.

From every village through which the party traveled similar groups joined him. The gentle manner of the friar seemed to appeal to the natives and they followed his every word and gesture with keenest interest.

Having crossed the Rio Fuerte and traveling from twenty-five to thirty leagues northwest, Fray Marcos came into the country of the Mayos. He found little difficulty in carrying on conversations with these people. The viceroy's Indians in his escort were of the tribe and stock of Sonoran Pimas or Nebomes, therefore their language was affiliated with that of the Mayos, as also of the Yaquis. Some of these natives, too, attached themselves to him.

At this point in the march Fray Marcos received a visit from some Indians who told him they lived on an island a short distance off from the mainland, and had made the crossing on rafts constructed of strong fiber and cord.

At about the same time another group arrived from a large island lying to the north. As interpreted, the information they supplied was as follows:

"They say that their homes are situated farther to the north than those of the first group. Beyond it there are thirty other islands; they are small, but they, too, are inhabited. Only two of them grow any food products, and these two bear only maize."

The island visitors wore numerous conch shells, formerly enclosing pearls, about their necks. When Fray Marcos showed them a pearl he had in his possession, they told him that there were similar jewels on the islands which they had mentioned. These islands, as he learned later, were strung along the coast of lower Sonora, between the mouths of the Mayo and Yaqui Rivers. Certain of them were inhabited by a fierce tribe known as the Seris.

The visiting natives further explained that the inhabitants of the first group of islands were Mayos, some of whom dwelled there permanently, others of whom only visited there to fish.

Fray Marcos was now traveling along the coast a short distance from the mouth of the Mayo River. From the information he had already picked up, and from still other indications, he correctly believed that the Indians of Southern Sonora [of Cáhita stock] or the islanders who were their neighbors, must be familiar with coastal navigation, and made use of rafts to pass from one point to another.

He was wrong, however, in his further deduction that the first group of visiting Indians lived on an island which had been visited by Hernando Cortés. He was later to learn that they inhabited the rocky islands south of the outlet of the Rio Petatlán, a place of many lagoons and sandbars.

Some of the Sinaloa Indians, he discovered, cremated their dead. Others buried them, usually under a tree. Entering a little settlement toward evening, he witnessed such a burial ceremony. All the Indians had gathered about the grave, which was heaped with the belongings of the dead. Blankets, feathers, bows and arrows comprised the collection. At one side was placed a quantity of food and a large hollow calabash containing water. If the dead man had possessed any dogs, the Pimas informed Fray Marcos, these would be killed, according to the native custom.

After leaving the island natives Fray Marcos and his caravan trailed for four days across a cheerless country. Occasionally they met a group of Indians, who gave them cheering news, telling them of a better country that lay ahead of them, four or five days' journey into the mountains, whose inhabitants were very intelligent people.

This information was confirmed when Fray Marcos

came out of the desert and saw the friendly natives hastening to meet him. They expressed astonishment at his presence in their country, crowded about him, patted him on the shoulders, took hold of his robe, and called him *Sayota,* which in their language signified "Man from Heaven."

The Pimas in the friar's escort could interpret readily the statements of these natives. It was evident to Fray Marcos that either the language of the newcomers was affiliated with their own, or else that they were familiar with it through dealing with tribes which employed it.

The zealous spiritual son of Saint Francis told these natives about "our Lord in heaven, and His majesty, the King, on earth." They listened attentively, and, when he had finished, hastened to their houses, where they secured large quantities of food and presented it to him.

Fray Marcos instructed one of the Pimas to bring forward some of the metals he was carrying. "I wish to show them to these Indians and find out whether they are acquainted with them," he said.

The Pimas followed his instructions. When Fray Marcos exhibited his collection, one of the natives took from it a piece of gold and held it up. Through an interpreter he told the friar that the people living in the region of which he spoke wore ornaments made of this metal hanging from their noses and ears. They were accustomed to fashion it into small blades which they employed to scrape the sweat from their bodies.

"Try to find out more about this country," the friar said to his Indians.

The natives, however, could add no more to their previous statements except the facts that the inhabitants of that place wore cotton garments, and that their towns were numerous and wealthy.

Estevan the Moor voiced his discontent when, after

hearing these things, Fray Marcos expressed his determination to remain near the sea coast, rather than go in search of the supposedly wealthy towns that were identical with those for which he was sent to search. Apparently, they were situated some distance inland, and his orders were to proceed directly in search of "the seven cities" of which Alvar Núñez Cábeza de Vaca had told. Schooled to perfect obedience as a religious, no thought of doing anything different entered his mind.

"The people in the towns these natives mention are Pimas, as we are," one of Fray Marcos' Indians informed the friar. "They belong to the Nebomes branch of our tribe, and are an agricultural people. They make pottery, dress in cotton and skins and wear many fine ornaments. They live in the valleys on the middle Rio Yaqui and carry on irrigation by means of artificial canals. Many of their houses are of adobe, and they are large and well built. There is a very large and strongly-constructed house in the center of their village; this is used for defense; when they are attacked, the inhabitants retreat to it."

For three more days the march continued through country dominated by the Yaquis. Although they appeared well disposed toward the friar and his party, these natives had long hated and feared white men. They had not forgotten the dastardly incursions of the men of Nuño de Guzmán, and the hard fight with his forces from which, after a brief test, the Spanish arms had emerged victorious. From that time until the present the Yaquis had not encountered white men, and they were wholly unfamiliar with their ways, though they cherished still a superstitious dread of them.

Fray Marcos admired the strength and purpose of the Yaquis. Their tribe was split into a number of self-governing villages, each ruled according to the tribal system.

The entire cluster came together only at intervals, and for some special purpose, such as self-protection. Their bravery in the field caused them to stand out above all the other tribes of the northwest coast of Mexico. Unlike the other Indians of that region, who lost their spirit when they witnessed their comrades lying slain about them, the Yaquis, in like circumstances, would leap over the dead and fight furiously.

Various Indian tribes designated their males by the number of victims each had slain in battle. This was particularly true of the Yaquis. They also bestowed names upon their children in memory of the places where they had killed their foes. Because of this, their tribal names were similar and often repeated.

The Yaquis spoke in high-pitched voices, inflecting their sentences like the Latin. They were possessed of fine physiques and were energetic and determined. Fray Marcos found, however, that, like the other tribes of this part of the country, they, too, maintained the unpleasant habit of eating rats, mice, snakes, worms, and vermin. Their principal diet was wild fruits, grain, fish, roots, and larvae.

Nowhere in this region did it appear that the natives made use of metals. When Fray Marcos showed his collection to them he noted that they judged all metals merely by their exterior appearance. The Yaquis manufactured a kind of pottery, generally yellow, sometimes of micaceous clay, which presented a dazzling surface when the sun shone upon it.

The Yaqui dwellings were fairly substantial, whether constructed of timber and adobe, or of plaited twigs, thickly plastered over with mud. They were one story high, with flat roofs. Although every Yaqui family possessed a dwelling, the tribe spent most of their time, especially in the summer, out of doors, under the trees.

This people did not seem to indulge in sports. How-ever, in some of the houses Fray Marcos saw grotesque masks. He was told that they were used in dances and ceremonials. Often the horrid sight of human bones and hair, suspended from the walls of the houses, proved a sorry reminder that the Yaquis indulged in hideous and fiendish rites when celebrating their war victories.

From the heart of these little villages, fields of maize, beans and squash stretched away into the distance.

"The Yaquis grind their maize in pottery bowls with a wooden mortar," the Pimas told the friar. When the latter witnessed the operation for the first time he was im-pressed by the fact that up to this point in his journey he had not previously noted the mortar in use among the Indians.

On the whole, he found the towns of the Yaquis better than those of the natives of Sinaloa which the caravan had left behind.

The Yaquis carried on trade with the north. They manufactured fabrics out of cotton and agave fiber, in-cluding blankets and serapes, making use of colored threads as decoration. They also made a sort of matting out of reeds and palm leaves. Their loom consisted of four short sticks driven into the ground, with a frame attached to hold the thread. The shuttle was an oblong piece of wood, on which the thread was wound. After passing through the web, the shutter was seized and pressed by a ruler three inches in breadth; this, placed between the web, supplied the place of a comb. When patterns were to be worked, several of the Yaqui women assisted in marking off, with wooden pegs, the amount of thread required.

As he continued his journey, Fray Marcos found that in many places visited the thrilling account of the seven wealthy cities was repeated. This fact in itself impressed

upon his mind the thought that the stories must be sub-
stantially true. To be sure, the Indians were notorious liars
and enjoyed nothing so much as magnifying a tale or in-
venting something they might add to it, according to their
fancy. Fray Marcos de Niza, intent on the high purpose
of his mission, did not always advert to this well-known
fact. So his zeal and ardor burned higher with each retelling of the welcome story.

For the following three days the caravan wound along
through a settled country. Here, also the natives were
cordial to the newcomers. They brought out skins and turquoises and loaded Fray Marcos with these valuable gifts.

With no little disedification and distrust the friar
noticed that Estevan's eyes glistened with ill-concealed
envy and desire as they rested on the treasures. In particular he was sorely displeased to find that the black
man was making very free with the Indian women, some
of whom followed him as he traveled from place to place.
Realizing anew his dependence upon the man, Fray
Marcos was afraid of incurring his enmity by censuring
him too strongly for his faults.

Deeply concerned for the salvation of the natives, the
Franciscan herald continued to show his crucifix to all the
Indians whom he met. It seemed to hold a strange fasci-
nation for them. They were delighted when he blessed
himself with it, as he was constantly doing. They tried to
imitate him in the act, and many of them hastened to
fashion small crosses of their own. Fray Marcos knew that
with such meager instruction as he had time to give, they
could not possibly grasp its true meaning, but it seemed
to him that they felt it was a profitable thing to bless
themselves with the cross. No doubt it was made clear to
them what a different significance the cross of Christ
possessed from their own primitive symbol. The cross as
employed by them indicated a star. The crosses in use

to represent the morning and evening stars were usually distinguishable from one another by their shape and color.

Fray Marcos planted Christian crosses all along his route and was pleased to find them treated with universal respect. Many of the Indians put up small grass huts expressly for the purpose of sheltering the cross. They watched the Christianized Pimas in the friar's company with interest akin to envy as the latter made the sacred sign upon their persons when reciting their prayer in common, morning and evening, led by their revered superior.

At this time Estevan approached Fray Marcos with a tale very surprising to the friar.

"The Indians say that the people of the seven cities wear robes of gray cloth like your own, Father," the Moor exclaimed.

Fray Marcos later learned that the garments of which Estevan spoke were blanket robes made of narrow strips of rabbit fur and yucca fiber.

His own cherished robe was now covered with dust stains and torn in numerous places. Each evening a part of his routine was to renovate it for the next day's work. Never before had it seemed so dear and valued as now, when it afforded never-ceasing inspiration and comfort in the hard journey to a far-off goal. *Nihil volitum nisi praecognitum* — "Nothing is desired unless it be previously known." Countless times had Fray Marcos read these words in his Rule Book, but never had they possessed more significance than now. Religious poverty, the badge of his Order, was most precious to him, for he was a true son of the Seraphic Francis, the "Poor Little One." In spirit he heard again the admonition of that holy father:

"Let all the friars be clothed in sackcloth and other pieces, with the blessing of God."

Not Don Antonio de Mendoza in his audience chamber

in the Casa de los Cabildos, ruffed and starched and jeweled; not Don Francisco Vásquez de Coronado, wearing the proud star of his forbears as he appeared by the side of his noble Beatriz possessed anything so desirable.

VIII

ALTHOUGH it was Fray Marcos' intention to remain near the sea coast, he was now swerving toward the interior. At the end of three more days he arrived at Mátapa, an Indian settlement forty leagues distant from the Gulf of California. The region was fertile, and the natives raised crops by irrigation, so that the place was well supplied with food.

It was now the middle of April, two days before Passion Sunday. From Culiacán, whence he had set out early in March, Fray Marcos had traveled a distance of five hundred miles to Mátapa. Although by the straightest route the journey covered no more than three hundred and thirty miles, yet when made on foot, by a more circuitous route with occasional stops for rest it was a slow process.

The village of Mátapa, located in central Sonora, afforded the friar and his followers a favorable opportunity for a little much-needed repose, as well as for the gleaning of information which must prove useful on their further adventures.

This village was a settlement of Eudeves, who employed a dialect of the Opata language, an intermediate shade between the Opata and Pima. As in the case of all the native tribes met so far, these Indians were very friendly toward the strangers.

The main source of disturbance for Fray Marcos was Estevan the Moor. The friar felt bound to watch him more closely as the days succeeded one another. His overbearing manner, his avarice and selfish ambition boded no good to the best interests of the expedition. The "Mexican With the Black Beard," as the Indians called him, continued to attract to him the Indian women of the villages through which the party passed; these women followed him in ever increasing numbers. They showered turquoises upon him, so that by now he had a goodly stock of the jewels stored in his belongings. A part, however, he had appropriated when the opportunity of so doing presented itself, and he was careful to lose no such opportunity.

Fray Marcos was not unwilling to rid himself of the near presence of this dangerous Moor by sending him on ahead as a scout, giving him explicit directions as to what he was to do. Estevan was to go to the north, fifty or sixty leagues, to see if in that direction anything of note might be observed, or some rich and well-settled country could be discovered. If he found anything or heard of anything of that kind, he was to stop, and to send a message to the friar by the Indians. This message was to consist of a wooden cross, of a white color. In case the discovery was of medium importance he was to send a cross of one span in length; and if more important than New Spain, he should send a large cross.

Estevan left Mátapa on the afternoon of Passion Sunday. His superior, having given him final injunctions and his blessing, noted with some trepidation the look of ill-concealed triumph on the dark-bearded face of the man, wreathed in the perpetual scowl common enough to his race.

Estevan listened with apparent respect to the admonitions of Fray Marcos. His quick brain, however, was con-

juring up a picture far different from that in the mind of
the latter. Released for a time from hateful supervision,
he sensed that his chances of winning personal glory and
treasure were considerably increased.

Gone were the days when, in his native country, he had
slept in the streets, wrapped only in his wretched gown.
Gone were the days of wandering, a miserable slave, in
the company of Spanish masters, the members of Cabeza
de Vaca's salvaged party. Instead, as soon as the slender
gray-robed figure of Fray Marcos, with the calm countenance and grave reproaching eyes, would be lost amid
the green fields, Estevan might begin to live — master of
himself and of his destiny.

Because his people belonged to the most polite race in
all the world, the Moor did not forget his manners now.
He knelt on the earth at Fray Marcos' feet, kissed the hem
of the coarse robe, and vowed obedience to instructions.
He was sincere in this, for as yet he foresaw no difficulty
in the path of fidelity.

From Mátapa Fray Marcos sent Indians of his party
to the coast to explore and find out the nature of the
islands of which the visiting natives had spoken. The distance from Mátapa to the sea coast facing Tiburon island
was exactly forty leagues, or one hundred and ten miles.
Tiburon was separated from the mainland by not more
than fourteen miles of sea.

The Indian scouts returned after a week's absence. In
their company were natives from the seashore called Pintados, or "Painted" Indians, because of the elaborate
decorations painted all over their bodies; also members
of the Seri tribe, a wild group who held sway not only
over the islands but also over the mainland shore.

The Pima interpreters made known to the friar what
these visitors reported.

"They say that there are thirty-four islands and islets

strung close together in their territory. These islands grow
no vegetable foods. The people living on them, and also
their kindred on the coast, hold intercourse with one
another by means of rafts. The Seris live from the hunt
and from the fisheries; they sometimes barter with the
upland tribes; they exchange fish, conch shells and other
sea products for maize and various commodities raised or
manufactured by the natives on the continent. They are
notorious thieves and are hostile to all other tribes."

The weirdly decorated visitors from Seriland listened
calmly to this account, given in Spanish, of which they
could not understand a word. When it came their turn to
speak, they informed Fray Marcos through the interpreters that the conch shells on their foreheads contained
pearls. They spoke in tones harsh and guttural, seemingly
suited to their savage tribe. The viceroy's Pimas informed
Fray Marcos that the language of these people was not
related to any of the other linguistic groups of Mexico. A
few words, frequently repeated by the Seris and accompanied by gesticulations, soon came to be understandable
to the friar. *Tanjajipe*, for instance, signified that they
were well satisfied with their reception by the white man
and his followers. *Jiciri* meant their people, either those
living on the coast or those on the islands. By *Amen* they
made known their wish for some particular thing, as for
the food given them by their hosts. *Migenman* signified
room or chamber — they repeated this word over and over
as they examined with great curiosity the dwellings of the
Eudeves, doubtless contrasting them with their own
shabby and unsubstantial bowers. A few other words of
their limited vocabulary, such as designations for food and
similar necessities, were readily recognized by the friar
after frequent repetition by the Seris.

The Seris called themselves Kin-kaak, or Kmike, their
common title from the Opata; it meant "Spry." Their ter-

rain was shut away from the settled part of Sonora by a
desert very difficult to cross. Their country was arid,
rough and unfriendly, chiefly desert and ragged rocks. In
but two or three places within it was water to be found.
The prevailing vegetation was perennial, but stunted in
growth; appearing in isolated tufts, it straggled over the
plains sparsely, disappearing altogether in the driest sections. The mesquite tree flourished over the other species,
its roots sometimes extending downward for from fifty to
seventy-five feet. The Seris ate the hard small beans em-
bedded in the woody pods.

Nearly all the plants in Seriland, the Pima scouts reported, had a highly offensive odor. Except in the moist
seasons, the trees were practically leafless. Not even in
the oases was there any green grass; only in the friendly
shade of shrubs or in a few scattered directions over the
damp portion of the land did fresh blades appear.

The homes of this people were always located miles
distant from the *tinaja*, or water spring. When they
wished to secure water it was necessary for them to walk
a long distance to these springs, carrying pots for the
purpose. They had no domestic animals except dogs,
which were largely of coyote origin.

The Seri visitors were men of imposing physique, with
fine chests and strong slender limbs. Their hands and feet
were disproportionately large for the rest of their bodies,
yet average in size. They walked with a vigorous stride,
were erect in carriage and exceptionally fleet footed.
Their clothing consisted solely of a makeshift skirt
wrapped around them and reaching from waist to feet;
this skirt was woven of coarse threads of string made from
native vegetal fibers. Several of the group wore pelican
skins instead of the woven robe. All had a belt around the
waist, generally a snakeskin, but in the case of a few of
them Fray Marcos observed that this belt was composed

of human hair. The head, feet, bust and arms of all the Seris were bare.

One of the Pima scouts continued the relation of the adventures of his group in the homeland of the Seris.

"They are a wild people, Father. Their houses are shabby huts made from cactus or shrubbery and shingled with shells or sponges. These suffice as shelter, for there is no rain in Seriland. When a family moves out of a dwelling, and that happens often, another takes it over and lives there. The Seris use stone implements to crush their food products, and also to grind up human bones and flesh. The women wear even more paint on their bodies than do the men.

"When we reached their territory they were conducting a funeral service. The dead man had been clothed in his best garments, and folded up into the smallest possible compass before being placed in the grave. The grave was shallow and, after the body was deposited in it, it was covered with turtle shells. Earth and twigs were then placed over the shells as protection from wild beasts. A small idol, with the bows and arrows and other personal belongings of the dead, was placed on the grave. The bodies of the Seri departed are never cremated; generally the burial place is a cave under a rock."

The Pima stated that other Seris lived on a large island in the bay; these came over to the mainland in graceful *balsas.*

"The balsas are rafts, Father, and are made of two cylinders of metal or wood, joined by a framework of mesquite fiber cords. They are built especially for easy landing in the surf. These *balsas* are three times a man's height and taper at each end. They can carry four or five men and are propelled by a double-edged paddle, held in the center and worked alternately on each side."

Fray Marcos was prepared for the next disclosure.

It appeared that the Seris, like many other tribes, smeared their arrow points with a deadly poison, taken from rattlesnakes and other venomous reptiles. These reptiles were teased by the Seris, then incited to strike their fangs into the liver of a deer or cow placed in their path. The mass was then left to putrify, later placed in the sun to dry. When this process was completed, the arrow points were dipped in the poisonous matter. The wound they inflicted, however slight it might be, caused death.

Fray Marcos had reason to suspect that the arrows carried by his Seri guests were the same death-dealing implements as those described by the Pima. But he maintained calm as one of the strangers exhibited his arrow with no little pride, pointing to the tip and shaking his head vigorously as if to indicate that for the accomplishment of its purpose, it could not be equaled. The arrow was pointed with flint, Fray Marcos observed, and fastened to a piece of hard wood. This was tied by sinews to a reed, with a nock in the other end, and had three bright-colored feather vanes. The Seri illustrated how, when the bow was not in use, the tying was loosed and the arrow point reversed, to protect it from breakage. A notch occurred a few inches below the point; the intention of the Seris was that when it struck it should break off and remain in the wound it caused.

The Pima continued:

"We noticed that some of the Seris carried clubs made of a hard wood called Guayacan, having knobs at their end; when not needed, these clubs are slung on the arm by a leather thong. Their lances are made of Brazil wood, and their bucklers of alligator skin. They carry shields of bulls' hide large enough to protect their entire bodies; in the top of these shields is a hole through which they can look. Some have another kind of shield, made of small lathes, closely interwoven with cords in such a manner that when not being used it can be shut up like a fan and carried under the arm."

When one tribe wished to help another in some emergency, reeds filled with tobacco were sent to the friendly group in need of such service. If the reed was accepted, it was a sign that an alliance had been formed between the two groups.

"A call for help is made by means of a signal," the Pima said. "When war is decided upon, a leader is chosen. The elders, medicine men and principal warriors assemble at his house. A fire is lighted and tobacco handed around; this is smoked in silence. Then the chief or the most illustrious warrior rises and in loud tones and most impressive language addresses his audience. He reminds them of the brave deeds accomplished by their ancestors, of the victories they have already gained and of the threatening wrongs of the present which must be avenged.

"War councils go on for several nights. A day is set apart on which the fight is to begin. Sometimes the enemy is told of this date, as well as the location where the encounter is to take place.

"All during this period of preparations the Seris observe a rigorous fast.

"They always approach the enemy in darkness, maintaining a strict silence. At daybreak, by a prearranged signal, a swift attack is launched. Sometimes the enemy's house is fired with lighted corncobs, carried on the arrow points.

"When the Seris are forced into retreat they carry off their dead with them; they consider it a point of honor never to leave the bodies of any of their group on the field.

"The Seris treat their war prisoners with terrible inhumanity. They show no respect for age or sex. All prisoners are handed over to the Seri women for torture. The women treat the victims most barbarously. They heap all kinds of indignities upon them, burn their flesh with lighted brands and in the end start a fire about them at a stake, or sacrifice them in some other ghastly manner."

Fray Marcos' face was very grave as he listened to the Pima's recital. The missionary heart within him yearned over this savage primitive people. Perhaps the Seris who stood by, scrutinizing him with no little curiosity, sensed something of this, for an expression of sympathy was registered in their faces. Dramatic as well as tragic figures they were, in the waning light of day. Their faces were striped perpendicularly, in some cases with red and black paint, in others, with blue, white, and red. Their long hair was gathered and tied in tufts on the crown of their heads. In their large hands the death-dealing arrows gleamed ominously.

While his heart melted in pity for the sad plight of these miserable specimens of humanity, Fray Marcos was pleased to realize that the Seris had come with friendly intentions from their distant wretched abodes to visit him. He showed them his crucifix and instructed his Pimas to try to make them understand its meaning. More he could not do, except to ensure that they were well treated while they remained in his caravan, and pray for the day of their conversion to Christianity.

The Pintados, whose faces and chests were decorated with incisions into which paint had been smeared, as well as several of the Seris, expressed the wish to travel with the friar, whose gentleness had completely won them.

Fray Marcos gladly granted the permission.

IX

RELIEVED of the embarrassing presence of his superior, Fray Marcos de Niza, Estevan the Moor felt his spirits rise at every step that took him northward from the valley of the Sonora. With him was a group of Indians who could serve as capable interpreters when he should reach unfamiliar tribes along the way. He also took a brace of greyhounds he had picked up earlier in the journey.

Estevan relied principally for success in the expedition on the fact that he had accompanied Cabeza de Vaca and the other white men of the Narváez company, saved after shipwreck, into that territory previously. The Indians among whom he should pass, knowing this, would be certain to treat him with respect. That, at least, he could count upon. The Moor was not displeased when now and then the natives came long distances merely to see him and touch his garments. In some cases they came into enemy territory to accomplish this end, so that their desire to meet the "Black Mexican" was greater than their fear of peril to themselves.

While he had been very anxious to rid himself of the friar, Estevan cherished a certain veneration for Fray Marcos de Niza. The gentle and mortified religious had often refrained from chastising his subordinate when the Moor transgressed, as frequently happened. Here and there along the way Estevan was careful to halt and, with the aid of his followers, set up little bowers to serve as night shelters for the friar when, later, Fray Marcos should pass that way.

The black man had outfitted himself with rattles, bells and plumes, which he attached to his legs and arms. So the former slave, captured over a quarter of a century before by Christian zealots who snatched him from his Moslem masters, was now equipped in gorgeous array. As he went along the way he attached to himself more Indian women and confiscated more turquoises. With a gourd, decorated with red and black feathers, in his hand, he proclaimed himself to be a healer, or medicine man.

When, at nightfall, the little band paused to rest, the Moor enjoyed another triumph. The role of storyteller was well suited to his emotions and talents. He told the Indians much about the far-off country from which he had come. It was a country where an honest man was assured of success, a dishonest man, never. Estevan told the truth in this part of his story. There were, he said, many blind beggars in Morocco; their eyes had been burned out with red-hot pokers by the Berber chiefs of the mountains. However, that was not the punishment meted out for a first offense. At the first theft, for instance, a man's hand was cut off. At the second, he paid the penalty with his eyes. Sometimes a foot was amputated, and the victim was thereafter obliged to walk with the aid of crutches.

The Moor had a motive in narrating these things to the members of his group. He carried with him many splendid turquoises, and he wished to impress on the Indians the fact that he, too, could punish theft, if occasion should arise.

When the "Black Mexican" sat, he doubled his legs under him, so that his beard brushed his knees. Like all Moors, he was inordinately fond of sweets — because of this passion his teeth were very poor. He rarely smiled, but his forehead was wrinkled with scowls. The hardships of his life in the New World had not greatly troubled him; he was used to sleeping on the ground from childhood and to bearing many other inconveniences.

To the simple-minded natives who crowded around him to listen to his fantastic tales as they rested after a long day's march, he said nothing of his poverty-stricken youth. He said nothing of the stone huts, whose chinks were filled in with mud and whose roofs were straw-thatched. His own home, one of a collection of straw shacks in a Moroccan village, was no part of him now. In its small bare yard sheep, goats and pigs huddled in the stark nights. The poorer people of the country lived most squalidly. In place of such scenes, Estevan described, as best he could, with the poverty of Indian words, the homes of the wealthy class; their treasures of carved wood, the rich mosaics and tiles in the great palaces, secure behind impregnable walls. At the fine brass tables Moorish gentlemen sat in rich gowns and pale lemon-colored shoes; the women in silken robes and red slippers of soft Moroccan leather. He described the stately camels strutting though the streets, and the pasturelands where flocks of goats grazed peacefully in care of their keepers.

His people, so the Moor informed his awestruck audience, were vastly superior to the Negroes, whose ancestors came from across the Sahara Desert in lands bordering on the Gulf of Guinea. The Berbers had brains, like the whites, he averred. The only black Africans in Morocco were those brought across the desert to the Sudan to be sold as slaves.

When night fell, and sleep closed the eyes of the Indians, Estevan did not as quickly sink into unconsciousness. Instead, he often sat, cross legged, on the earth, staring into the night with eyes large and bright. He never felt any compunction for the lies he told, or for the property he had appropriated unlawfully. His sole thought was to enrich himself in far greater degree in the near future.

As he looked from the brilliant sky to the earth, Estevan's keen eyes espied a cluster of thorny cat-claws, spread out close beside him. He drew a branch toward him, and, detaching a handful of the woody beans, munched them with now and then a grimace, as the hard gritty substance touched some sensitive spot in his gums. Beyond the cat-claw, struggling tufts of Sonora greasewood stretched away and creosote brush sent forth its distinctly disagreeable odor — in the light of the moon its bright green leaves were like silver. The pale tint of the cactus stems was lost in the gray of the fast-darkening landscape.

The cactus reminded Estevan of something. . . .

Hedges of cactus surrounded the straw shacks of a Moroccan village. As a boy, he had often stung himself on the sharp thorns. But they did not hurt as much as did the sight of Christians, walking by, or the despised Jews in their long black garments that swept the dirt. All Moors nourished a fanatical hatred of Christians. Estevan was now a Christian, but he had no reason to regret that fact. His life at the palace of Viceroy Mendoza was not to be despised, while his present superior, Fray Marcos de Niza, was a kindly amiable man who, when he was not doing good to others by the exercise of some useful office, was busy reciting his prayers.

But what of the seven cities? It was not long before one of the Indians, whom Estevan now met for the first time, told him a piece of news which appeared to be the best possible he could expect to hear.

"From this place," the Indian related, "it is a thirty days' march to the first city of the country called Cíbola. In that first province there are seven large cities, all under one lord. The houses are of stone and lime, and large; the smallest are of two stories, with flat roofs. There are other houses of three and four stories. The house of the lord is five stories high. All these houses are arranged in an orderly way. The sills and doors of many of the principal structures have figures made of turquoise stones, for there is a great abundance of those stones in Cíbola. The people of these cities are very well clothed. There are other cities beyond Cíbola that are even more important and rich than these."

Estevan was entranced. With the aid of two of his Indians he immediately fashioned a cross as tall as a man. This he entrusted to his messengers, telling them to go quickly to Mátapa, give the cross to Fray Marcos de Niza, and report the wonderful news about Cíbola.

"Tell the friar," the Moor said to the messengers, "that he should now follow me, and that one of the Indians who goes with you to see him has been to this rich province."

No sooner had the messengers departed than a sudden thought came to the mind of the astute Moor. He was fully aware that Fray Marcos could reach the spot where he himself now was in three days' time, once the Indian runners had conveyed the message to him. But why wait for the coming of Fray Marcos? When the friar should appear on the scene, Estevan's role of commander of the little troop of scouts would be ended. This idea was not to his liking. His eyes glinted with cunning as he considerd what he would do.

Upon receiving the message sent by the black man, Fray Marcos de Niza would surely start at once on the way to join him. The friar would leave the cool refreshing pueblo, well irrigated by the Opatas, a watered level high above the torrid desert country. Over grassy plains and oak-studded heights he could swing directly into the lovely valley of the Sonora.

But — the Moor had no intention of waiting for him until he arrived. With some of his Indians, he would push on, leaving others to greet Fray Marcos de Niza. Estevan knew that to execute his design was to disobey orders. Yet the thought of discovering the marvelous cities by himself, and the consequent glory which would accrue to him, overpowered all other considerations. The friar, Estevan told himself, would be so thrilled with the seven cities that, far from punishing his servant, he might even praise and highly reward him.

Curling himself up in a knot, his mantle drawn closely about his gaunt form, Estevan the Moor closed his eyes and fell asleep to dream.

He dreamed that he was drinking boiling hot tea in a palace in Morocco, at a brass table, most beautifully carved. There were many candles on the table, so that its carvings glittered in the flickering light.

But a sudden wind sprang up from nowhere — and all the candles went out.

X

ON THE SECOND DAY after Easter Fray Marcos de
Niza left Mátapa. The words of the Easter Sequence were
in his heart:

*"Surrexit Christus, spes mea: praecedet vos in Gali-
leam."* Christ, my hope! — in the remembrance of Him,
His servant, who deemed himself a most unworthy member of the illustrious Order of Saint Francis, went forward
in great eagerness to his goal. Christ, who had overcome
fear and darkness and sin and death; who ever went before His faithful servants, to light and guide them on their
path, would protect His own and lead him to the shining
land of his desire. For there were countless souls to be
won for Him in that distant land to the north. The divine
Saviour willed that they should be brought to Him. In
His loving condescension He had chosen Fray Marcos de
Niza to open the way to that glorious conquest.

Fray Marcos took with him two of the Seri Indians, who
seemed to have lost much of their wildness as a result of
their association with the little band. He also allowed
three of the Pintados, the Painted Indians, to accompany
him. With these new allies and his interpreters he started
over the trail which the willing feet of Estevan had trod
a little more than a week before.

Marching for three days, the party came into the village
where the Moor had first heard the news of the country to

the northward. It was situated high up in the picturesque valley of the Sonora River, near Babiacora. The natives knew about the seven cities, and they corroborated the stories concerning them as previously told to the friar. These Indians were the Opatas; Fray Marcos found them to be a highly intelligent and industrious people.

The gorge of the Sonora appeared majestic in its repose, especially when the full rays of the sun rested upon it. The depressions between the sierras, in other places no more than tiny canyons, were in this verdant spot wide and alive with vegetation. To westward, beyond the range of lofty hills, lay a broad coastal plain, broken by smaller ridges. The whole terrain resembled a gigantic accordian, with flutings running from north to south. Over the first range, to eastward, lay the Valley of the Sonora River. Into this earthly paradise the friar and his Indian escort had now penetrated.

The season was mild, but not yet hot. Along the Western Slope the surface was dry save where little rivulets, left from the winter rains, moistened the beds of the streams. The pipe-organ cactus was beginning to send forth virgin sprouts and the vermilion-colored flowers of the ocotilla splashed the gray of the hills like daubs of paint on a huge palette. In the sky lazy clouds floated, reflected in the shining lagoons beneath great cottonwood trees.

Like his Seraphic Father, Saint Francis, Fray Marcos de Niza appreciated at its fullest the handiwork of the Divine Artist. He was charmed by the loveliness of the landscape on which his eyes now feasted. True, the sturdy shrubs and brilliant blooms did not possess the tender grace and softness of the hedges and vines of his native Savoy, with its coronets of Italian May, its roses and carnations, violets and mignonette, intermixed in exquisite array. Here, instead, was a rugged grandeur, a lonely beauty, in which the tracery of God's art was even more apparent.

Once more the Indians of this place repeated the tales concerning the seven cities, precisely as Estevan had relayed them. These wonderful towns were situated no farther north than a thirty days' journey.

Even a few more items were forthcoming, to Fray Marcos' great joy. One of his Pimas informed him of certain statements made by an Opata Indian:

"He says that the houses are very large and high, and that Cíbola is the first of the Seven Cities. Besides these, there are other 'kingdoms' called Marata, Acus and Tontonteac."

The friar inquired why the Opatas went so far from their homes to distant countries. The reply was:

"They go in search of turquoises, cowhides and other useful and valuable things. There are plenty of these things in Cíbola."

Fray Marcos asked what was given to the inhabitants of Cíbola in exchange for their treasures. The answer was:

"The Opatas give the sweat of their brows and their personal service. In the city called Cíbola they serve the people by digging in the ground and doing other laborious works. In exchange for this labor turquoises and cow skins are given them."

The Opatas confirmed what the friar had previously heard, to the effect that the people of Cíbola wore many fine turquoises, hanging from their ears and nostrils, and that the principal doorways of the place were ornamented with them.

As to the dress of these people, the friar was told that:

"They wear a cotton shirt which extends to the ankles. There is a button at the throat and a long cord hanging from it; the sleeves of these shirts are of equal width from shoulder to wrist."

Fray Marcos de Niza wondered a little about what he had heard. It seemed incredible that the Opatas should go so far from home to labor for strange tribes. He believed that, when they stated that they dug turquoises out of the soil with considerable effort, they must have made use of hammers and axes for the purpose.

The Pima continued to interpret the Opata's words to the friar:

"He says, Father, that the natives of Cíbola also wear girdles of turquoises and very good mantles over their shirts; some wear cow skins, well prepared — they say there are many in the land. The people of Cíbola have the greatest esteem for these cow skins. The women dress like the men, and are clothed from head to foot."

Fray Marcos could not convince the friendly Opatas that he was unable to cure their sick by laying his hands upon them and praying over them. They insisted that he could do so. He complied with their request, and gave their invalids his blessing.

Some members of the tribe brought him specimens of the cow skins. They were very well tanned and dressed. These skins had come from Cíbola, the Opatas said. Actually, they were buffalo skins.

The friar was sorely displeased to find that Estevan had not waited for him here, but had gone on before, contrary to his orders. Himself obedient in the least things as in the greatest, he found this defection a burdensome trial. He was somewhat relieved that messages arrived almost daily from the Moor. Some of the Opatas had gone on with Estevan, so Fray Marcos learned. They had left four of five days previous to his coming here.

In many spots Fray Marcos found crosses planted by his scout, most of them large. It seemed that the Moor was anxious to persuade him that the news concerning Cíbola was the best possible. He had left word that his superior must make haste, so that he might the sooner reach the wonderful cities. Estevan assured him that he would be waiting for him at the end of the first desert, beyond where the friar now was.

So enraptured was Fray Marcos with the beauty of the Sonora Valley that he took formal possession of it, as Viceroy Mendoza had instructed him to do in the event that he came upon a country which seemed to him better than any he had previously found.

He greatly enjoyed his visit to the country of the Opatas, even though his thoughts dwelt principally on the Seven Cities of Cíbola. The unique Indian tribe who inhabited the fertile country around him here grew maize in large quantities and carried on highly successful irrigation. The Opata women as well as the men worked in the fields, cultivating, also, beans and squash. In particular, the friar enjoyed the taste of a favorite dish in these parts, called pinole. It was fashioned from parched maize, ground with a wooden mortar and sweetened with the flour made from the mesquite. Some mescal, also, was raised. This, the natives explained, was derived from either of two cactaceous plants, whose stems or joints were rounded and covered with tubercles. The tops of these tubercles were called mesquite buttons.

Unfortunately, drunkenness was common among the Opatas, as among the other tribes. The same mixture of maguey, mesquite and tunas was utilized to make the liquors.

These Indians manufactured some pottery, and they were very dexterous in managing *balsas*, like the Seris of the west coast and its adjacent islands.

Traveling through this tranquil valley, Fray Marcos was careful to learn everything possible about the natives who were his friendly hosts. He discovered that the bravest among them was always chosen as chief. This office was not hereditary, therefore, but the chiefs were selected for valor, or for having large families, or even because they were good talkers.

Their towns were well populated, with sometimes as many as five hundred houses in a single settlement. While they had no sacrificial customs, they made use of the services of shamans, or medicine men, the priests of the tribe. They believed in visions and dreams and kept idols and fetishes.

Throughout Sonora the customs were in some respects similar to those the friar afterward found distinguished the people of Cíbola. In the morning the dignitaries of the pueblos would ascend certain terraces, assigned for the purpose, and remain there for an hour, crying out to the natives what they must do. Temples were set aside in little houses, and many arrows driven into the outer walls, so that they resembled porcupines. This custom of driving arrows into the temples was especially prevalent when the Indians of the settlement were contemplating war or were certain of waging war in the near future.

The Opata Indians carried on some trade with the pueblo region to the north, and with the Cáhita to the south. They ate fish, and sometimes utilized them to make their arrow poison.

While passing among the Opatas, Fray Marcos learned with deep interest and some alarm of the existence of a tree known as the Poisonous Tree. It grew all the way from the Sonora Valley to Cíbola, for three hundred leagues, and in many other places. The natives asserted that it was the most terrible and deadly growth in existence. Unless one was fully acquainted with its properties, it might easily prove to be a deadly attraction. For it was perennially green and in season covered with flowers. It was two estados, or about eleven feet in height, and had pale green leaves. Natives who had the misfortune to fall asleep under it puffed up and soon died from the effects of the poison injected into their bodies by breathing the noxious scent. It held a white sap, coagulated like sour milk. The Indians who used it for their arrow poison were accustomed to make an incision in the vine-covered bark, which they called the herb of the arrow. They would then dip their arrow points into the sap in order to bring their enemies to a terrible death. The wounds inflicted by these points caused such intense agony that those so poisoned died in violent convulsions.

"If the wound occurs on the head or arms," one of the Pimas explained, "the Opatas say that the flesh corrodes, then rots and drops off. This happens even though the poison may only have touched an open wound for an instant and so come in contact with the blood stream. And they say that when it is brought near a wound, or close to human blood, it rushes to it with fearful speed, as if it were a living thing."

The Pima explained that the natives felled this tree from a distance by throwing stones at it. When it was prostrate, the milky sap which was to furnish the arrow poison trickled out. If the branches of the Poisonous Tree were cast into any body of water, they destroyed whatever life might be in it. In that event, the water touched by the branches would also kill any living thing that came into contact with it.

Scarcely any vegetation grew beneath or very near this horrible tree. It never changed or shed its leaves, like other trees, and when any kind of change did take place, it was so slow that it was not perceptible.

The Pima continued:

"The Opatas say that there is a root which can cure a wound infected by this poison. The name of the root is the caramatraca, and it bears a yellow flower. But even when this antidote is applied, the wound made by the arrow must be cut out and the parts affected tied with strong cotton and covered with raw corrosive sublimate twice, or until the damaged flesh disappears."

Whatever Fray Marcos might think of all this, it was apparent that there were many perils lurking along the path he was yet to tread before reaching the Seven Cities. But his mind was free from any distrust or thought of evil to come. God's providence was over all, and even in this primitive country he could offer up the adorable Sacrifice of the Mass in the early morning, when circumstances permitted him to enjoy that wonderful boon. Come what might, the courier of God and of the servants of God would fulfill his role faithfully and well.

Looking upon the precipitous walls of the mountains that hemmed in the green valley, Fray Marcos noticed a strange, many-hued vegetation clinging tenaciously to them. So, thought the man of God, the soul of the Christian, and particularly that of a friar, must cling to Him through every vicissitude of this mortal journeying.

In the midst of the gentle Opatas Fray Marcos experienced the greatest contentment he had so far enjoyed on the journey. Here was a vast field for the future endeavors of apostolic missionaries, who had God's glory and the salvation of poor pagans deeply at heart. Soon, with His help, these tribes, now ignorant of their eternal destiny, would have the Word of God preached to them and would hasten to rally around the standard of the Cross of Christ.

XI

THE OPATA INDIANS were pleased by Fray Marcos' kindly consideration and concern for their interests. The gentle-mannered friar had won the hearts of the simple primitive children of this gracious valley. They showed their happiness in his friendship by treating him with the utmost courtesy and generosity.

They told him that other branches of their tribe lived on the Upper Yaqui River; these Indians were more distant from one another than were the groups dwelling on the Sonora River, where the friar and his party now were. The former natives were divided into small settlements and were constantly at war with one another.

Fray Marcos could not rest here, however, for the glorious goal was too near. Still pressing northward, the little caravan entered a new and uninhabited stretch of territory, through which they proceeded for four days. The rising spirits of his Indians, especially those who had joined the group since the departure from Culiacán, indicated their delight at the thought that soon they would enter the rich and beautiful cities beyond. Treasure untold seemed there to beckon them, and they quickened their pace in the ardor which their expectations aroused, so that the friar had hard work to accomodate himself to their steps. The desert waste they now crossed was not treeless, but it was a country having no human habitations, with mountain chains towering above, rugged and wild.

On the seventh day of the march through this valley, the party entered the last Opata village, on the Upper Sonora. Here, also, the Indians came out to greet the white man, showing him every mark of hospitality and friendship. Tired though he was, and suffering from numerous aches and pains incidental to the hardships of the journey, Fray Marcos was rejuvenated by this kind treatment. It seemed that the people of Cíbola, also, must show equal friendliness to the emissary of the noble viceroy, the herald of the emperor himself. His heart was warm with gratitude for these hopeful signs. The spiritual son of Saint Francis forgot his weariness and the occasional twinges in his joints, and beamed on the Opatas.

As in the case of the tribes already met, these natives touched the friar's robe, made of the cloth of Saragossa, which Governor Francisco de Coronado had given him for the journey. They told him that there was cloth of this kind at Tontonteac, and that all the natives there dressed in it.

Fray Marcos was amused by the remark — he laughed heartily. He informed the Opatas that what they said could hardly be true; that the Indians of Tontonteac probably wore cotton mantles.

The villagers insisted on their point, however. One said:

"Do you think we don't know that what you wear is different from what we wear? At Cíbola the houses are filled with the cloth we wear, but at Tontonteac there are small animals which furnish the material for the manufacture of the cloth you have on your body."

Fray Marcos replied that he had never heard anything like that before. Inquiring about the animals which were supposed to supply the material in question, he was told that they were of the size of the two Castilian greyhounds which Estevan the Moor had with him when he passed that way, and that there were many such animals in Tontonteac.

The friar could not imagine what sort of animals these could be. He thought it possible that the natives of Tontonteac were a sheep or goat herding people. Or — the material might come from the jack rabbit, which, he was told, greatly resembled the greyhound except that the jack rabbit was shorter in stature.

Fray Marcos found in this little village a shelter which Estevan had erected for him. He was thankful that the Moor had obeyed in this, at least. Similar shelters were strewn along the entire course of his journey. Yet Estevan's superior could not excuse the man's disobedience in proceeding farther than he had been told to go.

The friar had now come among the Sobaypuris, a branch of the Pimas. These Indians wore many turquoise ornaments on their persons. Some had as many as three or four strings of the green stones around their necks; others disported them as ear pendants and nose decorations. The women wore skirts and chemises.

At this point in his epochal journey Fray Marcos de Niza was greatly pleased to hear the very best news by far that had yet reached him. It corresponded perfectly to the tales previously told him about Cíbola, even including minor details.

Cíbola, it appeared, was very well known to all this tribe. They told Fray Marcos how its villages were laid out, with a plaza in the center of each. They also described the shape of the houses.

He remarked that the houses could not possibly correspond to these descriptions.

To illustrate their point, however, some of the Sobaypuris gathered a little soil and ashes, poured water on them, and, by mixing them together, showed the friar how the natives of Cíbola laid the stone for the foundation and erected the house, putting on mud and stone until the structure was finished.

Fray Marcos laughingly asked if the natives of Cíbola had wings, by means of which they could ascend to the upper stories of these houses. The Indians laughed in return, then described a ladder which, they said, the people of Cíbola used for the purpose; placing a pole on their heads, they showed the friar that such was the height from one story to another.

Here, too, Fray Marcos heard more about Tontonteac. The Sobaypuris stated that the dwellings in that place were similar to those in Cíbola, but better and more numerous. Tontonteac would seem to be a very large place, almost without limitations.

Returning from this side excursion toward the Gulf, the party proceeded down the valley for five days. Throughout this section the villages were scarcely more than barrios, equivalent to tiny sections of large towns, and located at short intervals from one another. The soil of the place was well irrigated, and the people knew about Cíbola, even stating that they had been there.

At one of these barrios an aged Indian approached the friar and through the *lenguas,* the Pima interpreters, entered into conversation with him.

The old man stated that he was a native of Cíbola, but had fled from the place because of some trouble.

He then went on to say that the lord of Cíbola lived in one of the wonderful Seven Cities; it was called Ahacus. Subordinate chiefs were in charge of the other cities. Ahacus itself was very large, having many streets and plazas and inhabitants. In some parts of it, he asserted, the houses were eleven stories high. On certain days of the year the principal men of the tribe came to this city.

The houses were constructed of lime and stone. Their entrances, as well as front walls, were laid in turquoises.

The rest of the tale as told by the old Indian refugee was no less extravagant. Fray Marcos did not know how much of it to credit, but the main facts agreed with what he had already heard.

Toward the southwest, the Indian continued, there was a kingdom called Marata. In former times there were many settlements of high-storied houses there. This kingdom was at war with the lord who ruled the Seven Cities. For this reason, Marata had lost much of its prestige and had declined, although it still continued to fight gamely.

The aged one further stated that toward the southwest lay a kingdom called Tontonteac. It was the largest in the world, as well as the wealthiest and most populous. The people dressed in cloth made from material like that worn by the friar; some wore clothing of a thinner material, such as was taken from the animals previously mentioned. The inhabitants were highly civilized.

Another very large province and kingdom was called Acus. There was also an Ahacus, which was one of the Seven Cities, and, indeed, the largest of them all. Acus was a province in itself.

The old Indian said that the clothing worn by the natives of Cíbola was as already described to the friar. Those of the people who lived in cities slept in beds raised above the floor and covered with sheets and other bedding.

If, said the old Indian, the white man would consent to take him along to Cíbola, he would gladly go.

Fray Marcos' head ached a little. He had had much excitement that day, indeed, at all times since the beginning of the journey, for the effort to unravel the mysteries of Cíbola was no easy task. It was difficult to dismiss the all-important subject even when he lay down to repose.

God's glory and the salvation of countless poor pagans was at stake, and his prayers were interspersed with ardent intentions for the successful outcome of this great adventure. Of one thing the friar felt certain — Cíbola must be a wonderful, rich and populous place, and a fit kingdom to take over for Christ and for the emperor.

Fray Marcos and his bodyguard rested three days in this most northerly village of the Sobaypuris. The group of Pimas inhabiting the San Pedro Valley of the modern state of Arizona north to the Gila River were delighted to have him as their guest. They were residents of Pimería Alta, "Upper Pimaland." They told Fray Marcos that their name originated from the word, Soba, which was the name of one of their chiefs.

The Sobaypuris informed the friar very fully as to the route he must take from their settlement to reach the Seven Cities; what villages he would find along the way; where it was advisable to pass the night, and where food and water could be found.

Fray Marcos cross-examined his witnesses carefully. He was impressed by the fact that all were in the most positive agreement about Cíbola. It seemed reasonable to conclude that they spoke the truth.

Before going on, the friar was shown a hide "one and a half times the size of a large cow." He was told that it belonged to a beast which had on its forehead a single horn that curved down to the creature's breast. Thence it turned up in a point which was so strong, so the Sobaypuris asserted, that it smashed everything coming in contact with it. There were many such animals in the country; the color of their hide corresponded to that of a goat, and the hair was a finger's length.

The Indians exaggerated the animal's size considerably, as well as exercised their imaginations in regard to the horn. Actually, the creature was the mountain sheep.

Many of the Sobaypuris expressed the wish to be allowed to join the friar's cortege. The permission was granted. Fray Marcos then personally selected thirty chiefs, ordering them to make haste and prepare themselves to leave. They did so and promptly appeared in their most gorgeous finery, covered with large turquoises. Some wore five or six strings of the stones about their necks. The friar also selected the needful number of the natives to carry the provisions for their chiefs and for himself. The Sobaypuris gave him venison meat, hares and partridges, which he was told were most flavorsome.

Fray Marcos de Niza learned that Estevan the Moor had taken three hundred natives, as well as provisions, with him as he pressed forward on what was to prove his last toilsome trip.

Along the way Estevan had sent back various messages to his superior. One of these was to the effect that the Moor had never detected the Indians in a lie. This assurance still more strengthened Fray Marcos in his belief that the Seven Cities were all the Indians said they were. He himself realized, on leaving the last village, that they had told the truth about his route, about the villages along the way, and the food and water supply he might expect to find. He had no reason to doubt anything else said concerning the object of his quest.

On the ninth day of May the friar entered the desert.

Traveling over a very wide and much-used road, the company arrived at a suitable halting place for dinner. There was water in the place; this the Indians pointed out. A shelter had been prepared for the leader of the caravan. Beside it was another, with indications that it had been used during the night by someone who came that way. That someone had been Estevan.

Twelve days' journeying through this terrain brought Fray Marcos de Niza the first sorrowful tidings he had so far received. Tragic, indeed, the news was, for not alone did it tell of a terrible catastrophe which had befallen, but it held out grave threat of ultimate failure for the entire expedition.

An Indian, the son of one of the natives who accompanied Estevan, met the caravan in the road. Fray Marcos was astonished and dismayed to note his exhaustion and complete dejection. His whole body, moreover, was covered, not with sweat alone, but with blood.

From this courier the friar learned the worst possible news.

IN JUBILANT MOOD Estevan the Moor had set out for Cíbola, the Shi-wo-na of the natives. His path led along a trail of dusty green sage, of stunted cedar and pinon; past ageless cliffs striped in bands of red and gray sandstone. Ahead were the dark mountains of Cíbola, covered with timber and rambling along to within some twelve miles of the settlement. Traveling toward these grim barriers, the Moor was too concerned with thoughts of new treasures to note how their shadows lowered over him like a menacing threat.

A grotesque figure he presented, covered with feathers and bells and pirouetting in the midst of his Indian followers. Like an untamed steed he pranced as he neared the goal of his desire. So far as his overt act of disobedience was concerned, Estevan had no qualms of conscience.

The pueblo which he was fast approaching was built on a small knoll, on the north bank of a river which had its source near one of the other villages, flowed through the province, and disappeared a few miles beyond. Estevan was quite carefree. Attracted by his lordly demeanor, his elaborate festive decoration and his band of followers, all eager to serve his bidding, natives from all the settlements through which he had passed followed him. They were quite willing to carry his belongings; they believed that in the care of such an extraordinary personage they need have no fear of an unwelcome reception beyond.

Ahead of him, the keen eyes of the black man discerned a group of enclosures varying in size, about two hundred feet below the village, on the plain. These were one-story houses, and, as Estevan shrewdly guessed, were used as corrals for defense and for security in time of warfare. Many of them were dilapidated, for in Cíbola the rainy season lasted several months of the year, and scarcely a day passed without violent storms arising. This necessitated great vigilance in guarding the property, and frequent repairs.

When he had come within a day's journey of Cíbola, Estevan put into execution a plan he had long carried in mind. He sent ahead messengers to interview the lord of the place. These messengers were instructed to inform that potentate of the Moor's coming. They were to say to him that the black man came on a mission of peace, and also to cure their sick.

To his emissaries he gave a gourd elaborately decorated with strings of rattles and two plumes, one white, the other red.

He had no doubt of the success of this little mission.

But it soon appeared that his plans had failed, for the messengers returned, post haste. Their news was of little comfort.

They told how they had reached Cíbola, and, on being admitted to the presence of the subordinate chief, had presented the gourd to him. He took it in his hand, examined it, then threw it on the ground in a passion of anger.

"I know these people," he had screamed, "for these rattles are not of our own make. Tell them to return at once to the place whence they came, or else not one of them shall remain alive."

When Estevan heard the news he smiled waggishly. "Don't be afraid," he said to the messengers. "This is nothing. Those who at first show anger always show great kindness afterward. Every time the Indians gave me evil words in my previous travels, it was a sure sign I would be well received by them."

The crafty Moor then asked for a full account of all that his Indians had seen in Cíbola.

The men of Cíbola were short in stature, the Indians reported. Their clothing consisted of a cloak, over which the skin of a "cow" was draped. They wore shoes of colored or painted skin and head bands across their foreheads. The women, they said, were light in color and of good appearance; they wore chemises reaching to their feet. Their hair was dressed in a peculiar roll or twist that stood out at the ears, and was adorned with many turquoises. The people sang to the music of flutes in which there were holes for the musicians' fingers.

"There are fowls aplenty over all the place," one of the messengers added. "We also saw some thirty hairy animals, like hounds; these were in the house of the chief who received us."

Estevan received this account with much satisfaction. If any premonition of impending evil came into his mind, he dismissed it at once. He was prepared to do what Cabeza de Vaca, his Spanish leader, had done — to show signs and wonders over the bodies of the sick and by this means impress the people with the idea of his greatness.

Nothing daunted, then, by the bad news he had heard, the Moor, with his Indians, proceeded on the way to Cíbola. He walked so quickly that all his bells and rattles sounded and all his feathers waved vigorously in the wind. Borrowing hope from their master's demeanor, the messengers danced along with him, their spirits considerably revived by the prospect of good things to come.

Arriving at the town, Estevan saw that it was surrounded by a wall. His practised eye noted that this wall showed evidences of skilled workmanship. Small chinking stones had been utilized to bring the masonry to an even surface after the larger stones forming the body of the wall were set in place. These little pieces, mosaiclike, were so perfectly fitted together that only the finest joints were discernible, with scarcely a trace of mortar. The chinking wedges varied in size to suit the interstices between the larger stones of the wall. A coating of mud was spread over all.

Estevan marveled at the houses. The adobe, mud and stones used in their construction, pounded into a rubble, cemented with ashes and smoothed off, shone in the brilliant rays of the sun like dressed stone.

The Moor thought there must be about two hundred of these thickly clustered houses in the place, rising, generally, to a height of several stories, and that the village might contain from seven hundred to one thousand Indians.

Entering through the gate in the wall, he noticed the houses more particularly. They were flat roofed and built about a principal court, the latter very irregular in form. Several smaller courts and alleyways led from it.

The doorways of the upper terraces, reached by means of ladders, were generally open; a few were covered by a blanket or rabbit-skin robe. These doorways were placed in the lee walls, and Estevan rightly guessed that this was done for the purpose of keeping out the prevailing southwest winds. His sharp eyes glittered with desire as he noted that these doorways were ornamented with turquoise matrix. In comparison with the huts of the Pimas of Sonora, these dwellings appeared magnificent.

As the newcomers entered the town, they found some of the people engaged in their superstitious rites of devotion. They were worshiping a little spring of water, offering to it small painted sticks, feathers, and a yellow powder which they had shaken from flowers.

Ushered into the presence of the chief, Estevan boldly stated his case. He termed himself an envoy of peace and good will sent by white men, one of whom, with his followers, would shortly arrive. He wished, he said, to befriend the people of Cíbola and, especially, to cure their sick of whatever ills might afflict them.

The old men and the caciques of the place listened to this extravagant statement with tongues in their cheeks. They believed with good cause that the Moor was lying; they fancied that he was a spy, come to gather information about them for those who would later arrive and crush their people. They wondered how it was that a black man should speak of white leaders who were supposedly his friends. They were suspicious and indignant when the Moor asked unconcernedly for some of their women and for turquoises in return for the good offices he proposed to perform.

The lord of Cíbola inquired about these brethren of Estevan's. The latter stated that he had an infinite number of them and that they had a great stock of weapons with them. They were not very far away, he assured his hosts.

Hearing this, the chiefs took no further time for deliberation. They acted.

To his infinite surprise and alarm, the Moor found himself taken into custody and placed in an unoccupied house outside the gate of the town. There they left him alone, but not for long. The chiefs returned and sat for hours in peculiar squatting fashion on their haunches, suffering no apparent discomfort, and questioning their miserable victim. When they finally departed, tight lipped and scowling, they left him to a sleepless and anxious night. He was hungry and thirsty — but his captors had furnished him with neither food nor drink. He was too unhappy, however, to concentrate on anything save the one thought of possible escape.

His wandering gaze fastened on a small door constructed of a single wooden slab, closing a rectangular niche high up in the wall. He rightly surmised that this was a receptacle for the safekeeping of valuables such as turquoises, shells and fine feathers.

Lying on the floor — for there were no furnishings of any kind in his prison — the unfortunate Estevan thought of Fray Marcos de Niza, the considerate superior who had trusted him and treated him kindly, and whom he had so flagrantly disobeyed. He wished now that he had not gone against the orders of that holy man, to whom this expedition meant so much in every way. Disaster had come as a result of his rash and insubordinate act. With all his unholy soul he was sorry that he had failed to obey. He regretted that he had not remained faithful to the Christian teaching. In a dim stupid way he realized that there was no security in wrongdoing. His remorse, evidently, was largely selfish, but it contained something of real contrition for his sins.

Where was Fray Marcos de Niza now? Hastening forward, no doubt, while eagerly anticipating some further good word from Estevan. Estevan could send no word — perhaps he might never again be able to send word to anyone.

He wished he were safe in his native country; that he had never left it for the hazards and hardships of this uncertain lot. In the village of Azamor, at the mouth of the River Morbeya, called by his people Muley bu Xaib, the life had been lazy and carefree.

To be a beggar at home, lying on his back in the sunshine and watching the camels lumbering in and out of the narrow lanes; watching the young Moorish boys at play in their white gowns and red fezzes, with the funny little clumps of hair growing at intervals on their heads as the vegetation grew in the valley of Sinaloa; watching the despised Jews slinking past in their prescribed garb of dingy black — how desirable a lot in exchange for the fate perhaps now awaiting him.

Cold sweat broke out over the forehead of the Moor as he thought of his dream on a certain night, a dream of candles burning, and of how, suddenly, they all went out and left him in the dark.

He thought of the grapes, said to be abundant in the country of Cíbola, and rolled his thristy tongue over his lips as he recalled that he might die of his privations and sufferings before help should come to him. . . . If only he could lay hands on one of the numerous fowls he saw strutting along the streets on his way to prison. Hunger was consuming him now. The old men and the caciques, he had noticed, were gay with the feathers of these birds, which they maintained principally to supply them with such decorations. But that could not interest him now.

So, in alternate fear and hope and in vain wishes, the horrid night passed. Morning came at last, and the first faint rays of the rising sun filtered through a chink high up in the wall of the hut.

At a little distance Estevan the Moor could hear the preacher speaking to the people from the highest rooftop in the village. Although he could not see them, all the Indians had come out of their houses and were seated on the ground, listening in silence. Wisely, their leader told them how to live rightly; they must observe certain laws, work hard, refrain from drunkenness and worse vices. They were on no account to practice human sacrifices.

Estevan could not hear the words, only the sound of the voice, droning on in stolid sequences. The companion-

ship of his greyhounds was denied the unfortunate man.
He wondered whether he would ever see them again —
it appeared doubtful. The old men and the caciques had
not thus far taken any pains to make his lot endurable.
His pangs of hunger grew fiercer, and he remembered
how, in captivity, Cabeza de Vaca had scraped the earth
for roots until his finger tips became mere bleeding stubs.
Looking down on the earthen floor, he realized that not
even that meager opportunity for physical comfort was
available here.

The Moor was unaware that all his Indians had been
sent back with the exception of several boys who were retained by the chiefs.

For three days the leading men of Cíbola visited their
prisoner and questioned him, each time departing with
more sinister looks. When they left him for the third time,
they did not close the door of the hut.

Estevan's bloodshot eyes followed their retreating figures as they stooped low at the entrance, then solemnly
filed down the path.

Exultation filled his soul. Now was the time to make a
dash for liberty. All his old assurance and audacity returned in one swift moment, to lend speed to his flight.

Dashing from the hut he saw a number of his Indian
boys awaiting him. But he had advanced only a few yards
when a flight of deadly arrows, winging from all directions, felled him to the earth. There he lay prone, face
downward, his breathless body pierced with a score of
shafts.

Fray Marcos de Niza had lost his scout, a most unworthy one, to be sure, but very useful as his interpreter
and messenger to the Indian tribes of the north. Later the
sorrowing friar was to learn that the body of the Moor
had been cut up into small pieces and distributed among
the chiefs of Cíbola, so that all might be assured he was

dead. This was done partly in retribution for his sins, of which the Indians ranked as most heinous the assaulting of their women, whom they loved, as they said, more than themselves. The natives of Cíbola each had but one wife to whom they remained faithful until death, and they were exceedingly jealous of the honor of their women.

Among the people, another story of the manner of Estevan's death was to be preserved and told to the children in perpetuity, as follows:

"It is to be believed that a long time ago, when roofs lay over the walls of Kya-ki-me [Hawikuh], when smoke hung over the house tops, and the ladder rounds were still unbroken in Kya-ki-me [when the pueblo was inhabited], then the Black Mexicans came from their abodes in Everlasting Summerland [Mexico]. . . . Then and thus was killed by our ancients, right where the stone stands down by the arroyo of Kya-ki-me, one of the Black Mexicans, a large man with chili lips. . . . Then the rest ran away, chased by our grandfathers, and went back toward their country in the Land of Everlasting Summer."

XIII

FROM THE INDIAN COURIER, covered with sweat and blood, who came to him when he was within two or three days' journey of Cíbola, Fray Marcos de Niza learned of the tragic killing of Estevan the Moor. It was a harrowing story, as the Indian told it. According to the account, when the black man was pierced to death by many arrows, some of the principal members of his escort stood near by. They, too, were wounded, in greater or less degree, and fell to the ground. Some of the dead fell on the living, and the latter, afraid to move lest they should be dispatched speedily, remained in that excruciating position all night. They did not see their leader, the "Black Mexican," but they heard a great uproar in the town and beheld many Indians, men and women, looking from the roof tops toward a certain spot. They were gazing on the prostrate form of the Moor, put to death because of his statements about his white masters and because of his cupidity and avarice. The wise men of the order of Ka-Ka saw to it that he would trouble them no longer. The lord of Cíbola himself kept several souvenirs of the dead man, one, a gruesome fragment of his body, the others a dog and four green plates — Estevan had given him the gifts in the hope of winning his friendship.

Hearing these sorrowful details, Fray Marcos was heavy at heart. He realized that any attempt to enter

Cíbola in the face of such an unfortunate happening would be most unwise. His death at the hands of the black scout's murderers would accomplish nothing desirable. It would not be martyrdom, for the chiefs would then be acting, not in hatred of the Christian Faith, but because they feared other white men might follow the friar and do injury to them. Moreover, the noble viceroy, Don Antonio de Mendoza, had ordered Fray Marcos to have a care for his life, which was of great value to the Church, to the Franciscan Order, and to the Emperor.

Fray Marcos de Niza was determined to obey these orders. However, he believed that it would be well to go forward until he could at least view Cíbola from a distance.

But now a new test of his courage and fortitude arose. In fear for their lives, his Indians refused to accompany him. They not only resisted his fervent pleas, but went so far as to threaten his life, which they proposed to sacrifice in retribution for the anguish they said he had caused them by reason of the slaughter of their relatives who had accompanied Estevan and shared his fate.

Fray Marcos de Niza pleaded with the brown men to alter their decision. He prayed ardently for help in this difficult and perilous hour. . . . Neither pleading nor prayers would soften them.

The Indians began to wail in most dismal fashion, lamenting for their dead, while the friar, in an agony of fear and apprehension, continued to parley with them.

"The Lord will not fail to chastise Cíbola," he said. "And, when His Majesty the Emperor knows what has happened, he will send many of his Christians to punish those people."

In answer to this argument, one of the Indians replied that there was no man who could resist the people of Cíbola.

"Father," an Indian convert warned, "these men have plotted to kill you, because, they say, on account of you and Estevan their kinsfolk have been murdered, and that there will not remain a man or woman among them who will not be killed."

Fray Marcos did his best to reassure the man and to pacify the others. Tears rained down his thin cheeks and his voice was broken with emotion. But, as in every difficult test, calm and courage came to him, as the comforting words of Saint Francis, words of faith and confidence, were whispered in the secret places of his being:

". . . to pray always with a pure heart, and to have humility, patience in persecution and infirmity, and to love those who persecute and blame us. . . . 'Blessed are they that suffer persecution for justice sake, for theirs is the kingdom of heaven.' "

One expedient suggested itself to Fray Marcos' mind. Calling some of his Indians to him, he ordered them to bring forward his packs containing all the articles he carried for his personal use and others intended for the Indians whose friendship he wished to win along his route.

When this was done, he opened the packs and divided all the treasures they contained among those who stood by. Dry stuffs and similar useful goods were soon disposed of, as lean brown fingers were thrust forward, that each man might receive his share of the prize. Soon everything, with the exception of the vestments for the Mass, had been given away.

Then Fray Marcos de Niza spoke to the crowd:

"If you kill me, you will do me no harm, because I will die a Christian and will go to heaven. But those who do this deed must suffer for it, because the Christians will come seeking me, and, although I would not wish it, they will kill you all."

The Indians listened this time with something of

respect. The treasure they had received had somewhat appeased them, although a few still grumbled and showed their teeth in anger.

Emboldened by their change of heart, the friar continued:

"I hope some of you will go with me to Cíbola, to see if any others of our company have escaped, and to obtain news of Estevan."

No one came forward to volunteer for this office.

Sorely disappointed, Fray Marcos preserved his interior trust and outward calm.

"Whatever you decide, I must see the city of Cíbola for myself," were his final words.

The brown men could appreciate heroism in any guise. They could, however, not make up their minds to do as he asked.

They replied that no one of them would go with him.

Seeing that he was determined to go alone, if that must be, finally two chiefs agreed to be his companions.

His heart singing with joy and thankfulness, Fray Marcos set out with these chiefs and his own Indian scouts and interpreters. The fear of what might possibly happen to him seemed for the time being dissipated. His sole consolation lay in the thought that soon his eyes would gaze upon the terrain where the Cross of Christ was now unknown, but where, surely, it would be planted. He had no doubt that God, who had graciously come to his aid in an hour of utter blackness, would safeguard him and his little company and lead them securely to their goal.

After the killing of Black Estevan, the people of Cíbola had made no attempt to follow the fugitive Indians who rushed back to rejoin the friar. Because of this, Fray Marcos deemed it safe to proceed with his companions. None of the Indians who had returned took pains to enlighten him as to the real facts about Cíbola — namely, that while it was true that a few turquoises were used in the embellishment of the doors and costumes of the inhabitants, and the houses were high storied and made of a composite of stone and lime, the pueblo was by no means wealthy or distinguished in any way, but a mean village, whose people worshiped the common elements.

Hastening across the thorny reaches of the desert just below Cíbola, Fray Marcos took no cognizance of the cactus spines that bored like sharp needles into his ankles as he sped along. His mind was filled with the thought of what lay before him, at the end of the long and painful journey.

When, at last, with his little company, he espied Cíbola from afar, the sun was spilling gold through the blue sieve of the sky high above what appeared to be a radiant and queenly city, situated on the brow of a roundish hill. To the friar, whose tired eyes rested upon it in the clear dry air, it seemed to be larger than Mexico, which had only about fifteen hundred wooden houses in that early period of the viceroy's reign.

Fray Marcos de Niza looked on towers and pinnacles piling up against the horizon and gleaming in loveliness, turquoise and pure gold. The sight filled him with rapture — he did not dream of the pain of mind and soul that was one day to succeed this hour of exultation.

Fray Onorato, now at home in the monastery at Jalisco, was not there to partake of the joy with his friend and spiritual father. By relinquishing the quest early in the journey he had missed great hardships — and Fray Marcos, knowing Onorato's state of health, could not be sorry for this.

To the chiefs who had accompanied him the friar remarked that this "treasure-laden" country seemed exceedingly beautiful as he viewed it from afar. They replied that it was the smallest of the Seven Cities; that Tontonteac was larger than all the rest, and that it had so many houses and inhabitants that it seemed without limits.

Once again Fray Marcos de Niza forgot to reckon with the character and reputation of his informants. As yet he had had no experience to prove that they told anything but the truth — even Estevan had sent back word that he had never found the natives in his escort to speak a lie.

As a religious thoroughly versed in the interior life, the spiritual son of Saint Francis knew how very near to pain is joy. How one brief hour, even moment, of pleasure, may be swiftly replaced by searing soul anguish. Yes, even love was pain, for the human heart is capable of an infinite number of variations, and it clings tenaciously to that which it desires and esteems. . . .

So, now, fear succeeded the brief moments of rapture Fray Marcos de Niza experienced here in the solitude of the Cíbola desert. He feared for his life, should any of the inhabitants appear and seek to deal with him as in the case of Estevan. Within those high walls rested ghastly trophies of one who had dared too much and suffered the loss of everything, even life, in consequence. Estevan's body was now no more — perhaps the very bones had been burned or given to the dogs.

However, Fray Marcos resolved to carry out the instructions of the viceroy in every detail, at whatever cost.

Gathering, with the help of his Indians, a heap of stones, he fashioned a slender cross from twigs, no better material being at hand. This he set on top of the mound. He then declared that he set up this cross and landmark "in the name of Don Antonio de Mendoza, viceroy and governor of New Spain, for the Emperor, our lord, in sign of possession, in conformity with my instructions." He declared that he took possession, then and there, of all the Seven Cities, and of the kingdoms of Tontonteac, Acus, and Marata.

Very hungry — for the food supply had run low — Fray Marcos then departed with his followers, to retrace his steps to Mexico, to the seat of the viceroy. He had fulfilled a mission of the eyes; he had looked on what he thought was beauty — but gold in the distance is not gold in the hand.

He left behind the deceitful vision of beautiful cities, shimmering in the roseate light; the cities of which Tejo, the Indian trader's boy, had told; the cities for which Cabeza de Vaca and other conquistadores had vainly sighed; which one sole inhabitant, an aged refugee Indian, had described in glowing terms.

Fray Marcos' feet were winged by fear for his life, and his heart was heavily oppressed, despite the joy of discovery, with the memory of Estevan's tragic fate.

As he took his way across the greensward, the sun's last rays fell aslant on the little cross of twigs he had set up on its lowly mound.

XIV

IT WAS NEAR the end of May when Fray Marcos de Niza first viewed Cíbola from afar. Hastening back over the trail to the southward, he found new trials awaiting him. The hospitality and kindness he had previously experienced from the native tribes along the way were now denied him. It was apparent that these Indians wished to have nothing to do with one whom they credited with bringing grave misfortune upon others of their race.

As the company advanced, they came upon two little shelters, constructed of twigs. Fray Marcos knew that they had been put up by Estevan, with the aid of his allies, as he forged ahead toward the Seven Cities, leaving his superior behind to await news of his findings. One of the shelters was obviously intended for Fray Marcos, the other for the Moor himself.

Peering through the opening of one of these shelters, the friar saw that the bed of leaves was tumbled. His scout had evidently slept there on one of his last nights on earth.

Fray Marcos' eyes filled with tears. The untimely death of the black man had shocked him unspeakably. He could only hope and pray for the salvation of the unfortunate who had blocked his desire to meet and converse with the natives of the Seven Cities and tell them of the eternal heritage that awaited them if they would consent to embrace the Christian faith.

His feet winged by fear and hunger, Fray Marcos traveled at a high rate of speed. Soon the party came into the midst of the Pimas of the San Pedro Valley. Here the saddened friar found that these Indians, too, who had formerly treated him with respect and confidence, remained aloof and evidenced no disposition to be friendly. Their villages were strangely empty as he passed through them, his gray robe trailing in the sand, The few natives whom he met or saw at a little distance turned quickly from him, or scowled as they searched his worn face with a sour expression in their narrow eyes. They were still mourning the death of their relatives and friends who had gone to Cíbola with the Moor, and they looked upon the innocent friar as the sole cause of their anguish.

In this valley the spiritual son of Saint Francis had met the aged Indian who had told him much about the Seven Cities. Now he looked in vain for that garrulous old man, thinking that he, at least, would sympathize with him. But he, too, was missing.

Another uninhabited stretch, the same he had traversed on the forward journey, brought Fray Marcos and his escort to a passage lying between bleak and savage mountains that now seemed to glower on him from their inaccessible peaks.

The little band stopped here to rest for a brief period. Fray Marcos sat down on a great stone to stretch his limbs and refresh his weary soul with a short meditation.

High in the foothills the saguaro cactus threw out its stalwart arms against the sky. On the mountaintops its high pillars with cruciform arms, silhouetted against a curtain of mauve and blue, were so many crosses on their separate Calvaries.

One of these great cacti shadowed the rock where Fray Marcos rested in the heat of the noonday. A monolith of jade green, its columns, fluted their entire length and

emerging from a stout trunk, grew separately to a height
of ten feet or so. Above these, the rugged arms were
thrown out from a spiny base, almost at right angles.
Thick sharp needles, growing in rows about the base of
the trunk, showed gray and purple. But like a great
candelabra was the saguaro in its bloom, each of its
branches terminating in the waxy whiteness of its clustered flowers. In the rainy season its ridges sucked in the
water, so that the plant retained abundance of moisture
to sustain its life.

If Saint Francis were there, Fray Marcos thought, he
would make friends with the saguaro.

"The holes you see, Father, bored into the columns," a
Pima Indian explained, "were made by woodpeckers. The
plant seals them over with a wax coating. Hawks make
their nests in the crotches of the branches, although, as
you observe, the branches are surrounded with sharp
thorns. For centuries my people, as well as the Yaquis,
have made use of the saguaro berries for food and drink,
though the plant bears little or no fruit until it is over
fifty years old."

Yes, Saint Francis would have made friends with the
saguaro, which in such absorbing fashion showed forth
the handiwork of its Creator. So thought the friar, and he
praised God in all His works.

Coming into the Opata village in Upper Sonora nearest
to Cíbola, Fray Marcos remembered how these Indians
had brought to him their sick. Now, however, they did
not come out from their dwellings to crowd about him
and touch the hem of his robe. Fray Marcos walked, a
lonely man, where once he had been treated almost
royally.

Despite his fears and misgivings, he determined to approach the open tract situated at the end of the mountain
ranges, peopled as it was for many days' journey toward

the east. So he had been told. But he would not enter it because he believed the Spaniards should give first attention to the Seven Cities and explore other parts afterward.

From the starting point of the trail Fray Marcos now saw what at some distance appeared to be seven moderate-sized towns, with a green valley, fair and good to the eye, lying beyond them. A great volume of smoke was rising from them. There, he was informed, a great deal of gold existed. The natives dealt in this precious metal, making vessels from it and selling them, also little plates with which to scrape the sweat from their bodies. However, they refused to have any dealings with the people in other parts of that same valley. Why, the friar did not learn.

He erected two crosses in the place and took possession of the plain and valley for Spain, as he had previously done at Cíbola.

Again past the gorge of the Sonora Fray Marcos de Niza trailed, and through the valley of the Sonora River. He paused only long enough to take the repose absolutely necessary to enable him to push on. So, back to Matapa he came, where he had rested during Holy Week, waiting for news of Estevan the Moor.

Through the territory of the warlike Yaquis he passed next. These Indians had shown themselves very friendly toward him as he journeyed north. Now he had no wish to test their loyalty, but hurried onward, holding little or no conversation with the natives whom he met.

Again he crossed a waste country, which seemed in a sense more friendly than did the villages, since here no hostile looks were directed toward him nor was he in fear of any dangerous move on the part of the inhabitants.

The friar and his company might have journeyed approximately ten leagues the first day of the return trip from Cíbola; then eight, again ten on the following days, without making any stop until they reached the second desplobado. Their average speed was, perhaps, twenty to twenty-five miles a day back to the Mayo River, the place where Fray Marcos was told it was a journey of thirty days to the Seven Cities.

A march of two more days brought him to the Indians he had left behind when he pushed farthest north. From this point on all traveled together until each group of natives reached its home along the route.

Fray Marcos expected to meet the young governor of Nueva Galicia, Don Francisco Vásquez de Coronado, shortly before the end of August, at the village of San Miguel in Culiacán, whence he had set out on his epochal journey. To his great disappointment, Coronado was not there but had gone to Compostela. The soldiers and villagers, however, were eagerly prepared to listen to the friar's account of his adventures. He did not linger long, for he was anxious to reach the governor and relate to him all that had passed since their parting.

At Compostela, Don Francisco received him, and drank in every word of Fray Marcos' relation with the utmost satisfaction. His fondest hopes seemed near to realization. He thanked the friar for coming to him with such pleasing news — news which he had reason to believe was to mean much to the Emperor and to the viceroy — as well as himself.

Coronado was well satisfied, now, that he had sent an optimistic message to His Majesty in a letter he had written at Compostela on July 15. In this letter, after acquainting the Emperor of the state of affairs in Nueva Galicia and of his visit to San Miguel for the purpose of ending the strife and bloodshed existing there, he added:

"I took with me to this province of Culiacán a friar of the Order of Saint Francis named Fray Marcos de Niza.

The viceroy of New Spain had recommended that I send him inland, because he was going at his command, in the name of Your Majesty, to explore, by land, the coast of this New Spain in order to learn its secrets and to gain knowledge of the lands and peoples that are now unknown. In order that he might travel with greater safety, I chose certain Indians from among those who had been made slaves in this province of Galicia but whom the viceroy had freed, and I sent them to the towns of Petatlán and Cuchillo, nearly sixty leagues beyond Culiacán. I asked them to enlist some native Indians of those pueblos and to tell them not to be afraid, since Your Majesty has ordered that no hostilities be waged against them or bad treatment accorded them, or that they be made slaves. In view of this, and of the fact that the messengers who came to appeal to them were free — which astonished them not a little — over eighty men came to me.

"After having taken particular pains to make clear to them your royal will, namely, that at present you do not want anything else from them except that they become Christians and recognize God and Your Majesty as their lords, I charged them to take with all assurance Fray Marcos and Estevan, a Negro, to the interior of the land. The viceroy bought the Negro for this purpose from one of those who had escaped from Florida. They did so, treating them very well.

"Traveling their normal days' journeys, the Lord willed that they should come to a country, very fine, as Your Majesty will see by the report of Fray Marcos and by what the viceroy is writing to you, and inasmuch as he is doing so, I shall not go into details here. I only hope that God and Your Majesty will be well served, not only by the greatness of the country which Fray Marcos tells about, but also by the planning and activity which the viceroy has displayed in discovering it, and that he will employ in pacifying it and bringing it under the authority of Your Majesty."

By word of mouth Fray Marcos de Niza had confirmed certain of the facts mentioned by the young governor in his letter to the Emperor. The noble don pressed the hand of the friar warmly as he assured him that he had done his work well. When the northern province should be conquered, then his own wish, as well as that of Fray Marcos, concerning the going of the friars to Cíbola, would also be accomplished.

Hearing from Fray Marcos' own lips further details of Estevan's death, Coronado believed there would be need of severe measures in dealing with the people of the Seven Cities.

XV

COMING into Mexico City at the end of his long and hazardous quest, Fray Marcos de Niza rested his eyes on scenes familiar and beloved from long association.

In the plaza the crowds were jostling one another, as of old. The drowsy burros dragged unwieldy little carts over the paths, and flower vendors bore panniers filled with a riot of colorful blooms, crying out their wares as they passed along. The welcome tolling of church bells broke like celestial music on the ears of the friar, who had missed it sorely during his exile in pagan and un-fruitful lands.

He did not linger to speak to those who approached him, but hastened to the palace of Don Antonio de Mendoza, the noble viceroy, to present his report of the journey to Cíbola.

Don Antonio was overjoyed to receive him. Governor Coronado, who was present at the reunion, witnessed the proceedings that followed with no little interest and gratification. Both the viceroy and his young protégé, Don Francisco Vásquez, believed that the important achievement of the friar augured great things for the Church and for the Crown, as well as for their own personal prestige and emolument in the near future.

"You have suffered, Father," the viceroy said, as he scanned the thin sun-tanned face of the friar. "Not alone from the difficulties and privations you were called on to endure, but, even more, from the tragedy of the Moor's death. However, great things are bound to come of your exploit. The greatest, as you are well aware, will be the Christianization of the northern tribes. This must come about when our arms have overcome the stubbornness of those natives."

Fray Marcos de Niza had prepared a report of his findings, somewhat abbreviated, but sufficiently comprehensive to reveal the principal happenings of the journey. This he now presented to Mendoza, after testifying, under oath, to the truth of what he had written.

The friar's statement began:

"With the aid and favor of the Blessed Virgin Mary, our Lady, and our seraphic father, Saint Francis, I, Fray Marcos de Niza, a professed friar of the order of Saint Francis, in fulfillment of the above-contained instructions from the illustrious Don Antonio de Mendoza, his Majesty's viceroy and governor of New Spain, set out from the town of San Miguel in the province of Culiacán on Friday, March 7, 1539, taking with me Fray Onorato as companion. I also took with me Estevan Dorantes, a Negro, and some Indians from among those whom the said viceroy had liberated and bought for this purpose. . . ."

Fray Marcos had found it difficult to write the names, "Onorato" and "Estevan," for both recalled poignant memories to his sensitive heart. Only the latter occasioned him deep sorrow, however — he had hoped for good things from the converted Moor, whereas the very worst had come to pass.

Continuing his account, Fray Marcos stated that he had gone on his way, in the above-mentioned company, to the town of Petatlán. He described the welcome everywhere accorded him by the natives, who greeted his arrival in their midst by showering gifts upon him.

"I was greeted along the way with many receptions and presents of food, roses, and other such things. And houses of branches and mats were built for me at all the places where there were no settlements.

"At this pueblo of Petatlán I stopped for three days because my companion, Fray Onorato, was taken ill, and I found it advisable to leave him there. Observing the aforesaid instructions, I continued on my way wherever the Holy Spirit, without my deserving it, guided me. I was accompanied by the said Estevan de Dorantes, a Negro, some of the freed Indians, and numerous people of the land. Everywhere they welcomed me with receptions, gladness and triumphal arches, giving me of whatever food they had, although it was but little, because they said it had not rained for three years, and because the Indians of that region put more effort into hiding than into sowing, for fear of the Christians of San Miguel, who used to come to wage war on them and take them as slaves. . . ."

Fray Marcos recorded that the Indians from an island came to see him. He described their appearance and related what they told the interpreters about their home and the islands adjoining it.

Then came the march of four days over a *desplobado*, a region unfavorable to habitation by human beings because of its barrenness — Fray Marcos did not fully describe it. At the end of this pueblo he met other Indians, who were astonished to see him, since it appeared that they knew nothing of "Christians." These natives, too, welcomed him most royally, giving him receptions and a great deal of food. "They tried to touch my garments and called me *Sayota,* which in their language means 'man from heaven.'"

Wishing to give them some idea of the Christian religion, although unable to remain among them to instruct and baptize them, Fray Marcos explained to them "as best I could, through interpreters, the significance of my instructions, namely, the acknowledgment they must make to our Lord in heaven and His Majesty on earth. I always tried by all possible means to learn about a country with many settlements and with people more advanced and cultured than those I met. I obtained no other information except that they told me that four or five days inland, where the cordilleras of the sierras end, there is an open valley. . . ."

At this point the friar related how he showed the natives into whose midst he had come some metals he had with him. Selecting from the collections some gold, they informed him that there was similar metal in the possession of the people of that valley. From it they fashioned vessels and ornaments for their noses and ears, also small blades for the purpose of scraping the sweat from their bodies.

The relation continued with the details of the journey until finally the settlement of Vacapa was reached. Estevan was sent ahead with definite instructions. He was to continue his journey fifty or sixty leagues northward, seeking information about the Seven Cities. Fray Marcos noted the size of the different crosses Estevan was to send back, according to the news he should hear. Four days afterward came a token of success — a cross the height of a man. Those who carried it to the friar, informed him "of the greatest thing in the world." One of Estevan's messengers had himself been to the Seven Cities. This Indian "told me so many marvels about the land that I postponed believing them until I had seen them or had further verification of the matter."

Fray Marcos set down in careful detail the wonders of this northern country, as the Indian messengers described them.

Three Indians from the Islands off the west coast, "Pintados," came to visit Fray Marcos, "because they had heard of me." Among other news, "they gave me much information about the seven cities and provinces of which Estevan's Indians had told me, and their accounts were about the same as those that Estevan had sent me.

"So I dismissed the coast people, except two Indians from the islands, who said they wanted to travel with me for seven or eight days. Accompanied by them and the three Pintados . . . I set out from Vacapa* on the second day after Easter Sunday, following the road and direction taken by Estevan. I had received other messengers from him, bringing another cross of the size of the first he had sent. He urged me to hurry, affirming that the land I was seeking was the best and greatest that had ever been heard of. The messengers told me individually what the previous one had said, without omitting the slightest detail; on the contrary, they told much more and gave a clearer explanation."

So the report continued, coming at last to the death of Estevan the Moor, and its sorrowful sequence.

Fray Marcos stated that from Compostela he had sent word of his return to Mexico to Viceroy Mendoza and to his Father Provincial, Fray Antonio de Cuidad-Rodrigo, of whom he asked what he was now to do. This request was in accord with his vow of obedience, and so far he had fully complied with its sacred obligations.

Concluding his relation, Fray Marcos testified as to the care he had exerted in trying to state only facts and to differentiate most faithfully between what he had actually seen or believed he had seen, and what he had learned from the Indians. . . .

"I omit here many particulars which are not pertinent; I simply tell what I saw and what was told me concerning

---

* Bandelier and others identify this with Matapa.

the countries where I went and those of which I was given information, in order to make a report to the Father Provincial, that he may show it to the father of our Order, who may advise him, or to the council of the Order, at whose command I went, that they may give it to the most illustrious lord, the viceroy of New Spain, at whose request they sent me on this journey."

Unlike Estevan, Fray Marcos had obeyed his instructions from higher authorities with ready and docile adherence. Now, in all simplicity, in the spirit of his holy Founder, he told what he had to tell. At the end of the document he affixed his signature:

"Fray Marcos de Niza, *vice commissarius.*"

The document of attestation was drawn up and signed by Juan Baeza de Herrera, chief notary of the audiencia. Another seal was placed on the document by Antonio de Turcios, also a secretary, who testified that he was present at the process and that he placed his seal "unto it in testimony of the truth."

Fray Marcos de Niza was pleased that these things were accomplished, and that he had carried out his instructions to the best of his ability as he had promised at the outset of his journey.

The high reputation which the friar enjoyed with Bishop Juan de Zumárraga and with the members of his own Order lent authority to his statements. Fray Antonio de Cuidad-Rodrigo, his Provincial, now came forward to testify once more to the unblemished character of Fray Marcos de Niza, no less than to his ability.

Setting his hand to the report prepared by the pioneering Fray Marcos, Fray Antonio wrote:

"I, Friar Antonio de Cuidad-Rodrigo, religious of the Order of Minorites and Minister Provincial, for the time being, of the Province of the Holy Evangel of New Spain, declare that it is true that I sent Fray Marcos de Niza, priest, friar, presbyter and religious, and in all virtue and religion esteemed; that by me and my brethren of the governing board, who take counsel together in all arduous and difficult matters, he was approved and held fit and able to make this journey and discovery, as well for the aforesaid character of his person, as for being learned, not only in theology, but also in cosmography and navigation."

This declaration was followed by some details regarding the friar's departure for the north. It was dated August 26, 1539.

Fray Marcos de Niza was deeply grateful for this testimonial to his character and work. Therefore, his ardor increased in what he felt was a great and noble cause, the spreading of the knowledge of the Seven Cities and the other provinces of the north, where an apostolic task awaited the ministers of Christ's Gospel.

The friar had reached Mexico on the return from Cíbola near the end of August, 1539. Soon the story of his adventures and the data he had given were noised about in many places. Not alone in the capital, but in Vera Cruz and Puebla de los Angeles was the story handed from one to another, never losing in the passage. In general, these tales were founded on what Fray Marcos had actually said — it was his honest opinion that Cíbola was a rich and important country; that it contained gold and precious stones in abundance, and that its people were of a superior culture.

One of the relators, Andrés García, gave testimony that proved highly satisfying to wide-open ears. García stated that his son-in-law, a barber by profession, had shaved the friar shortly after the latter's return to the capital city. The barber told his father-in-law about a conversation which, he alleged, the two men had at that time.

The witness testified that Fray Marcos said that after crossing some mountains, he came to a river having many settlements on its banks. These settlements were prosperous cities; they were encircled by high walls and their gates were guarded most vigilantly. Silversmiths plied their trade in the streets; the men wore gowns of white wool, with gold girdles, and the women wore strings of gold beads over their clothing. There was much livestock in the wonderful cities; this included sheep and cows, and there were also partridges. The Seven Cities boasted slaughterhouses and iron forges, with other amazing assets.

Fray Marcos de Niza certainly had failed to mention some of these wonders. No one would ever know how much of the story told by the barber was willful exaggeration on his part and how much was founded on what he actually believed he had heard. Every Spaniard to whom he told it was quite willing to believe all of it, for the minds of all were centered in the thought of the vast wealth recently acquired through the Spanish conquests in the land of the Moctezumas and the Inca princes. Why should not Cíbola equal in wealth and opportunity those subjugated countries?

Certain it was that the gentle little friar would not have recognized much of the relation, had he heard it repeated in his presence.

Meanwhile, he found himself in ever increasing demand as a preacher, for the entire population was aroused by the stories of the wonders of Cíbola. Occupying many pulpits in succession, the friar spoke to large congregations on the subject of the Seven Cities, especially of the great spiritual treasure awaiting there, the souls of poor pagans to be won for Christ; then, of the vast material resources to be utilized for the advantage, not only of its primitive possessors, but of the Church and the mother country, Spain.

Unfortunately for Fray Marcos, his reports were not only magnified by ignorant and lowly persons, but by those of high rank as well. Yet, because Fray Marcos was not a Spaniard, but a Savoyard, and because the Spaniards were jealous of their reputation for discovery and conquest and eager to claim the treasure about which everyone was talking, they had no special sympathy for the friar.

On his part, Viceroy Mendoza was glad that he could foresee no need of urging his compatriots to join in an expedition to conquer the Seven Cities of Cíbola.

Mendoza lost no time in forwarding the report of Fray Marcos to the king. Don Antonio was fully aware that, while it contained much valuable information, much of it was founded on hearsay, as the friar acknowledged. The latter had been principally concerned with reaching and entering the Seven Cities themselves, therefore, he had not gone to any considerable pains to learn the ethnological facts about the native tribes through whose midst he passed. He had told something about the Seris, the Opatas and the Sobaypuris, but little about the Indians of Sonora. Mendoza considered as of special importance the mention of the primitive intercourse between distant stocks and tribes and the commerce between these peoples. He realized that there might be some unintentional errors in the data as set down by the friar, since the tales told the latter on the journey were invariably embellished to suit the fancy of the tellers.

The most significant statement in regard to this commerce between tribes seemed to be that the Opatas and Northern Pimas were accustomed to travel as far north as Cíbola to exchange commodities. Of lesser importance was the fact that the wild Seris, living on islands off the western coast, traded with the inland tribes.

Don Antonio de Mendoza had reason to be pleased that Fray Marcos de Niza attracted to his pulpit great multitudes of the people.

XVI

THE MUSTERING of the great military force which was to follow the trail blazed by the spiritual son of Saint Francis of Assisi was speedily in process of formation. Mendoza's thorough experience in the country enabled him to realize that the journey could not be undertaken until spring, when the roads leading from the capital city would be passable. However, intensive preparations for the expedition went on apace. The armorer was busy night and day getting ready the equipment for the uneasy host of men who found it extremely difficult to remain patient under the enforced delay. In his audience chamber in the Casa de los Cabildos, Mendoza was frequently forced to cover his ears with his hands, to shut out the continuous thud of the armorer's hammer. None would be more thankful than the viceroy when the city should be rid of this tumult and distraction.

Don Antonio was anxious to see the last, for the time being, of the more than three hundred gentlemen of fortune who had responded to his call for volunteers to go northward. Among them were numerous disgruntled landowners, who, unsatisfied with their holdings, were feverishly intent on bettering their fortunes in a country they had reason to believe was exceedingly wealthy.

Don Francisco Vásquez de Coronado was rewarded for his patience and loyalty to his chief by being chosen leader of the expedition. The young man was the viceroy's best friend, and the former believed him to be sufficiently clever, prudent and generous to fulfill his commission with honor and success. Mendoza realized that parting for the time from the lady Beatriz would be a difficult trial for Coronado to face, but face it he must, as a Spanish soldier and gentleman, for the greater good of his country. If he accepted the commission, the young man must also leave his considerable estates for an indefinite period. Yet Mendoza had no fear it would be declined.

The viceroy knew that he had full authority to make this important assignment. By a royal cedula, issued on April 17, 1535, the king had shown his complete confidence in Don Antonio. His Majesty had also taken occasion to rebuke Hernando Cortés for his insistence on what he termed his "rights" to exploration in the north. This claim was based by the conqueror of Mexico on his appointment as captain general, in 1522.

The document of His Majesty, delegating authority to the viceroy of New Spain, read as follows:

"I, the king, to Don Antonio de Mendoza, our viceroy and governor of New Spain and president of our royal audiencia and chancellery there:

"Whereas you know that Don Hernando Cortés, Marqués del Valle, has been named captain general of New Spain, although, through the interpretations and limitations added later he can not discharge this function except by order of our president and judges, and in such cases he is to follow the instructions they may give him, and

"Whereas occasions may occur when it may be desirable to entrust the undertaking to some other persons, we by these presents grant you power and authority so that if an occasion arises when it may be desirable to entrust its execution and fulfillment to some person other than the said Marqués, you may have authority to act accordingly, as president, viceroy and governor.

"Given in Barcelona, April 17, 1535."

The royal decree confirming the appointment of Don Francisco Vásquez de Coronado as leader of the expedition to Cíbola was issued by His Majesty on January 6, 1540, who ordered his secretary, Francisco de los Conos y Molina, Knight Commander of the Order of Santiago in the kingdom of Leon, to prepare it under his direction. It gave to the young Coronado all the power he required for the prosecution of the momentous enterprise soon to be launched. In part it read as follows:

"I, the King. By order of his Majesty — Cobos — comendador mayor.

". . . So, considering it conducive to the service of God, our Lord, and our own that this said expedition be carried out in our name, and having confidence that you, Francisco Vásquez de Coronado, our governor and captain general of New Galicia, are a person who would properly and faithfully perform and carry out whatever we may entrust and commend to you, and that you will take special care in the protection and defense of the said lands and their natives, by these presents, affirming and confirming the said appointment made of you, the said Francisco Vásquez de Coronado, by the said Don Antonio de Mendoza, our viceroy of New Spain, we appoint you anew as captain general of our people who are now going, that may go later, or of any others you may find there, and of the lands and provinces of Acus and Cíbola, and the seven cities and the kingdoms and provinces of Matata and Tontonteac and of all their subjects and dependents; and of the other lands and provinces that you may discover or that may be discovered through your industry; that you command all the people who may go there, whatever their condition or state, that they follow and accept you, the said Francisco Vásquez de Coronado, as our captain general, and obey you, and respond to and perform your commands, and to respond and appear before you at your call at the specified times and under the penalties that you may stipulate and order, which by these presents we impose on them. We grant you power and authority to enforce these orders on those who may be rebellious or disobedient. . . ."

His Majesty issued explicit prescriptions for the appointment of the captain or captains agreeable to Coronado, giving the young don full power over them, as well as the commission to preside over all civil and criminal cases, and to select the lieutenant or lieutenants who should hear and decide these cases.

The king likewise gave orders as to the treatment of the Indians of those countries through which the army should pass. These instructions, bearing the viceroy's signature, were to be carried by Coronado on the march and faithfully executed, under prescribed penalties for failure to do so.

No person was to oppose these designs in any manner, but all were bound to accept the judgment of Francisco Vásquez and give him any assistance he should request.

Although every Spaniard was fully aware of the twofold purpose actuating His Majesty in commissioning the expedition to set forth, it was clearly stated in a paragraph concerning the command of New Galicia, which Coronado must leave in care of another during the period of his absence. . . .

"Inasmuch as you, Francisco Vásquez de Coronado, are our governor and captain general of the said province of New Galicia, and you are going, by our command and in our service, to the discovery and pacification of the said new land and to bring its natives to the knowledge of our holy Catholic faith and to bring the land under our royal crown, by this token we grant you power and authority that, during your absence from the province, you may leave and shall leave in your place a lieutenant or lieutenants, who shall be suitable persons, in the locality or localities where you may wish. And we order that such persons as you may have appointed in New Galicia shall be accepted, respected, and obeyed as lieutenant governors there."

Coronado's salary was fixed, also the right he had to the service of the Indians who should be assigned to serve him, "whether in New Spain or elsewhere. . . ." "Likewise, it is our will, and we so order, that the said lands and the others you may pacify and bring to our service as our captain general, you may retain until other arrangements are provided and ordered by us or by our viceroy in New Spain. You are to protect and defend these lands and their natives in our royal name in order that no injury or ill treatment may be inflicted upon them, and in order that no other persons may enter those lands and take possession of or occupy them, saying that the government of these new lands belongs to them, until, as has been stated, measures be taken that are most befitting our service."

This royal document was issued in the City of Michoacán, by Don Antonio de Mendoza, and duly registered.

It was to prove a bitter potion to the ambitious and jealous Cortés, and still further strain the relations already existing between the viceroy and himself, as well as foment in his mind further antagonism toward the lowly Fray Marcos de Niza, whose cause Mendoza, on the best possible recommendations, had espoused.

The viceroy deemed it wise that the choice of officers and captains for the expedition should be his own, not Coronado's. Those selected for offices of trust and responsibility must be wholly satisfactory to the entire army, so that none could question what they should do. Happily, Mendoza knew that he could count on unfaltering obedience and respect from every Spaniard in his territory. Not even a viceroy and favorite of the king could ask for more.

When first the news of Fray Marcos de Niza's discovery penetrated Europe, with it were heralded reports of Mendoza's extensive preparations for the expedition of conquest. Immediately a host of petitions and protests poured in to the Spanish sovereign. These emanated from persons who felt that they alone had the right to lead the army into the field where glory and emolument waited. All petitions were placed on file; they comprised testimonies regarding explorations made or purported to have been made by the claimants; "acts of taking possession of new terrain for Spain; notifications and decisions, appeals and countercharges." Meanwhile, the interested parties waited in fond expectation of a favorable outcome to their suit, part of a most complex business. Each claimant evidenced extreme jealousy of every other, and each succeeded in making himself, either personally or through a representative, an unmitigated nuisance to the Crown.

In the petition of Hernando Cortés the claimant stated that Viceroy Mendoza had ordered him to withdraw his men from the coast of the mainland, looking to the north, where he had been engaged in making preparations for exploration on a huge scale. This command had occasioned the utmost dissatisfaction and chagrin to Cortés, whose empty title, Marqués del Valle, brought him small consolation in the affair.

Fray Marcos de Niza, whom Cortés considered to be Mendoza's principal instrument of frustration to his hopes, came in for his share of accusation from the disappointed conquistador. The latter asserted that, following on his enforced submission to Mendoza's commands, he had met the friar. . . .

"And I gave him," he deposed, "an account of the said country and of its discovery, because I had determined to send him in my ships to follow up the said northern coast and conquer that country, because he seemed to understand something about matters of navigation. The said friar communicated this to the said viceroy, and he says that, with his permission, he went by land in search of the same coast and country as that which I had discovered, and which it was and is my right to conquer. And since his return the said friar has published the statement that he came within sight of the said country, which I deny that he has either seen or discovered, but, instead, in all that the said friar reports he has seen, he only repeats the account I had given him concerning the information which I obtained from the Indians of the said country of Vera Cruz, because everything the friar reports that he has discovered is just the same as what these Indians have told me: and in enlarging upon this and pretending to report what he neither saw nor learned, the said Friar Marcos does nothing new, because he has done this many other times, and this was his regular habit, as is notorious in the provinces of Peru and Guatemala; and sufficient evidence regarding this will be given to the court whenever it is necessary."

The Marqués del Valle did not enjoy a reputation for scrupulous regard for the truth. He was seeking by all means within his power to gain his end. Until now, when his personal fortunes were at stake, he had never taken pains to make public his story about his purported meeting with Fray Marcos, and the conversation which he alleged had then taken place between the two men. Boldly he proclaimed that, had not Mendoza prohibited him from making the journey northward, he himself would have found Cíbola and its riches.

Further elaborating on his complaint against the viceroy, Cortés maintained that not only did Mendoza place every possible obstacle in his path to prevent the execution of his design, seizing six or seven of the Marqués' vessels that had failed to get out of his reach in time, but the viceroy had sent a powerful force up the coast to prevent Cortés' ships from entering any port. When tempestuous weather forced one of these ships to put into Guatulco, the pilot and sailors were thrown into prison and the viceroy himself retained the ship, refusing to turn it over to its rightful owner. Also, Cortés stated, in the hope of obtaining information about his, Cortés', plans, a messenger whom he sent from Santiago in Colima was seized and tortured. . . .

Another claimant, less obstreperous, but equally insistent, was Hernando de Soto. He had recently received permission to explore the country between the Rio de las Palmas [modern Texas and Florida]. It was not improbable that De Soto might direct his forces toward the western limits of his territory, should he learn of the rich prospect awaiting there. Mendoza was unaware that De Soto had sailed from Havana in May of 1539, and that in July of that year, after sending back the largest of his ships, had begun the long march through the everglades which was to bring him in sight of the rippling waters of the Mississippi.

On behalf of De Soto, his representative stated that his client had an excellent argument to back up his claim, inasmuch as he could make a better financial offering to the crown to defray the expenses of the expedition than could Mendoza. In any eventuality, he said, the explorer would win acclaim for his exploit. But in the case of Mendoza, the viceroy must needs call on the crown to pay the entire expenses incidental to the undertaking — unless he were to pay them out of his own private fortune. If the viceroy did finance the expedition, surely at a later date he would endeavor to win back his outlay from the home government. In view of these facts, De Soto alleged that he was the better suited of the two men to undertake the project.

The outcome of these and suits similar in content was to be made known on May 25, 1540, when the Coronado expedition was fully under way. The decision was made by the fiscal, Villalobos, in his report on the matter. The whole affair had been referred to him on April 21, and about one month was required for the issuance of the final statement.

The licentiate declared that each of the parties that had set up claims had proved conclusively that none of the others had any right to make the explorations, and, consequently, to share in the spoils to be won. These parties were given an opportunity of replying to the decision. They continued to petition for a year longer, although the expedition to Cíbola and the other provinces was long over by the end of that time.

Villalobos had bluntly counseled His Majesty not to grant any of the privileges demanded by the claimants. He remarked that the discovery ought to be made in His Majesty's own name, since the region involved in the dispute was not included in any previous grant. Although the Crown had forbidden further unlicensed explorations, such an edict could not apply to ventures of the kind as undertaken by the Crown, because it was always free to exercise that privilege.

After this declaration, made formally, De Soto clamored more loudly than ever for the opportunity of going north, alleging again the fact of his ability to finance the project without aid from the home government.

There was no response to his claim.

Viceroy Mendoza had already won. He had organized and sent forth his army long before the court of Spain was fairly rid of its importunate claimants.

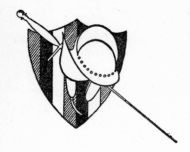

XVII

A SHREWD organizer and thorough statesman, Don Antonio de Mendoza decided that Mexico City should not be the starting point of the expedition to the far north. Considering the objective of the undertaking, the subjugation of Indian tribes and the seizing of their territory for the Crown, even on the most plausible allegation, the subsequent excitement resultant from it might well exercise an unfortunate influence on the Indians of Mexico City. The viceroy had no wish to jeopardize his influence over them. Therefore, he decided to send the army, in contingents, to the city of Compostela, the chief stronghold of New Galicia, situated at a distance of one hundred and ten miles from the capital. There they could form their ranks and proceed without embarrassment to the government authorities.

The viceroy had exercised his right of naming the principal officers, to serve under Coronado. Don Pedro de Tovar he made ensign general. Lope de Samaniego, then in charge of the arsenal at Mexico, was to be army master. As captains, Mendoza named Don Tristán de Arellano, Don Pedro de Guevara, Don García López de Cárdenas, Don Rodrigo Maldonado, and Diego de Alvarado. The captain of infantry was Pablo de Melgoas, and the captains of cavalry, Hernando López and Diego Gutierres. All the others appointed to positions of responsibility were, like the captains, distinguished either for valor in the service of their country or were members of families who had so distinguished themselves.

The viceroy was well pleased with his choice of this select group, chosen to lead the most noble company ever to assemble for service in New Spain. He had reason to hope for great things as a result of their endeavors.

Because some of the gentlemen to whom high office was entrusted were without funds, Mendoza distributed to them a portion of their salaries in advance, taking the money from the royal coffers for the purpose.

In groups, the eager, excited men of the army departed from the city. There was no official farewell, but Mendoza kept his palace during the exodus, occupying himself with whatever business came to hand.

When once again the capital had settled down to quiet, he sent for one of his trusted captains, Don Pedro de Alarcón, with instructions which were to be carried out without delay.

"You will take the two ships, now in the port of La Trinidad [on the coast of the South Sea] and sail them to the port of Xalisco, carrying the baggage the soldiers are unable to carry. You will sail along the coast, keeping as near the marching army as possible. I am told that our men will proceed through territory on the seacoast, and that we shall be able to find harbors by means of rivers. In this way we shall have news of the expedition at all times."

Mendoza believed this was possible — he was to ascertain at a later turn of affairs that it had no foundation in fact.

Anxious to view his army at its start, the viceroy now made hurried preparations for departure to Compostela. He had decided to accompany the men for a short distance in order to lend courage and enthusiasm to their enterprise.

At Compostela Don Antonio proudly reviewed the entire company of his soldiers. Drawn up in ranks for his inspection, it was apparent that all were in high spirits. The time had passed very pleasantly during which they awaited the coming of their chief. The official in charge of the government of the city for the time being, Cristóbal de Oñate, had treated them with all consideration. As the viceroy looked over the shining ranks, he was delighted with the execution of his plans thus far.

Fray Marcos de Niza, whose eyes had beheld that desired land whither the army was about to proceed, was not present. Eager to retrace the path he had trod less than a year before, at the cost of great sacrifice and peril to his life, he was pressing northward, in order to verify what he had already ascertained and by further observations pave the way for the expedition. With him were three other friars, Fray Antonio de Victoria, Fray Juan de Padilla, and Fray Luis de Escalona.

Mendoza made a careful observation of all his men. When he had finished, he assigned each captain to his post. His voice rang out strong and clear as he called the illustrious names:

"Don Pedro de Guevara. Don García López de Cárdenas. Don Rodrigo Maldonado. Diego López. Diego Gutierres . . ." and so to the end of the roster.

When all the gentlemen whose names were called had stepped forward in order and received their commission, the appointments were confirmed by Mendoza and Coronado.

The viceroy was relieved that he was now free from the temporary discomfiture he had suffered when the people of Mexico protested that all the able-bodied men in the capital were going from their midst, leaving them exposed to treacherous outbreaks on the part of the Indians. Coronado, instructed to make official inquiry into the matter, found that all those who were to accompany the expedition had volunteered of their free will, and that no pressure from any source whatsoever had been exerted on them to influence their decision.

Only the previous day, February 21, 1540, Coronado had appeared as witness at a hearing held at Compostela to present a petition to the viceroy in relation to the depopulation charges.

Juan de Leon, "their Majesties' clerk" of the royal audiencia, heard the deposition, which set forth the facts in the case. . . . Coronado deposed in part as follows:

"Information has reached me that some persons ill disposed toward this expedition . . . have claimed that many residents of Mexico and this city of Compostela and other cities and towns of New Spain are going on the said expedition at my request and urging; and that for this reason the city of Mexico and New Spain are left with but a few people, which may result in serious difficulties. In order that the truth may be learned . . . I beg and entreat your Lordship to order that a report be made of the matter; there are present here . . . his Majesty's factor and inspector in this New Spain, and other residents of Mexico, who will be able to verify the truth of everything and of the report. . . ."

On February 26, shortly after the army had left Compostela, the matter was cleared up to the satisfaction of the viceroy and that of the young general, Coronado, when a reliable witness testified that in the entire army he did not recognize any residents of the capital except a few who either did not permanently reside there or were going for some valid reason. Others followed this witness with similar depositions, and the case was dismissed.

This embarrassment cleared up, no further criticism was heard. Mendoza might have stated that in his opinion the exodus from the city of so many men whose lives were far from exemplary was advantageous, rather than detrimental to the general good. Henceforth his residence would not be choked up with a swarm of restive young idlers, impatiently waiting for some worth-while adventure to turn up. The viceroy, moreover, had but a slender supply of funds for the conduct of his private enterprises; now he no longer was obliged to cater to the whims of his unwelcome guests or to feed and lodge them at his own expense.

Green and sunny was the plateau of Compostela on the eventful morning of the army's departure for the north. Never had the sun risen on a spectacle more dazzling. The viceroy's gaze, however, was riveted on one man, the youthful Francisco de Coronado, sitting erect and proud on his splendid Andalusian horse, the noblest beast in all Mendoza's extensive stables. The general's gilded armor and plumed helmet singled him out from the rest of the company, as they were later to prove an excellent target for the enemy's shafts.

Drawn up behind their leader in imposing array, two hundred and twenty horsemen awaited the signal to start the march. Some of the group wore full harness of glittering mail, the rest, native buckskin suits. Holding their lances in upright position, and with bucklers showing at their hips as the gayly colored trappings of their mounts streamed in the breeze, they appeared a noble company.

Next in the ranks were the foot soldiers. Theirs was to be a particular wearisome role, yet it had its advantages, since it exposed these men to peril far less than their comrades on horseback. The pikemen wore iron helmets, as they stood side by side with the crossbowmen and harquebusiers, the latter bearing primitive firearms over their sturdy shoulders. Others carried swords of various type, as well as daggers and similar weapons of offense in common usage among the natives of Mexico.

Behind the footmen stood the Indians and Negro slaves. These men had charge of the pack animals and the bronze field pieces which the general expected to use, if necessary, in laying siege to Cíbola. The brown and black men were content with their role in the expedition, for they were bursting with confidence in the expectation of returning laden with rich spoils.

Mendoza was later to testify that there were more than one thousand animals — horses, mules and stock, in the caravan. When they were counted by his order at a certain narrow pass on the journey, it was found that the number exceeded fifteen hundred.

In the extreme rear one thousand Indian allies were drawn up, their shining bodies daubed in hideous streaks of black and ocher-colored war paint. They gripped their bows and slings and their wooden maces in grim satisfaction at the thought of using them to good effect when the occasion for so doing should present itself.

The viceroy had issued stringent orders that these allies were to be treated with kindness and consideration; that they were not to be made to bear any burden or suffer any indignity at the hands of the soldiers. Because of this order, the Spaniards were obliged to carry their personal baggage. They understood that the allies were free men, also, and as such were to be allowed to enjoy all the rights and privileges of the white men. If at any time they wished to give up the march and return to their homes, they were not only to be permitted to depart, but were to be given an armed escort to accompany them. In their packs they carried certain articles given them from the storehouses of the royal factor; they could exchange these for other goods with Indians met along the way. If any of the allies fell sick, every care was to be expended in order that they might be restored to health.

Mendoza and Coronado had previously examined the

official Muster Roll of the Expedition, dated February 22, 1540. The subtitle announced in formal manner that the official paper constituted "Testimony Concerning The People, Weapons, And Provisions That Set Out From Compostela In New Spain [When Don Antonio de Mendoza Was Its Viceroy], Taken To The Land Newly Discovered By Fray Marcos de Niza, Of Which Francisco Vásquez de Coronado Was The General."

Fray Marcos' name appeared, also, in the opening paragraph of the paper presented by Juan de Cuebas, chief notary of mines and reports in New Spain:

"I, Juan de Cuebas, his Majesty's chief notary of mines and reports in this New Spain, state and certify that at the city of Compostela in New Galicia of New Spain, there being present his Excellency, Don Antoino de Mendoza, his Majesty's viceroy and governor of this New Spain; Gonzalo de Salazar, factor; Peralmyndes Cherino, inspector of the said New Spain, and Cristóbal de Oñate, inspector of the said province, and many other people, a review was held of all those who are going to the land newly discovered by the father provincial,* Fray Marcos de Niza, of which Francisco Vásquez de Coronado is going as captain general. This said review was held on February 22, 1540, in the presence of the judge, Licentiate Maldonado, in the following form and manner. . . ."

General Coronado's name came first on the roll — his possessions exceeded somewhat in number those of his captains:

"Francisco Vásquez de Coronado, captain general, swore that he is taking on this expedition in the service of his Majesty twenty-two or twenty-three horses and three or four sets of weapons for bridle and saddle. . . ."

---

* The same reference to Fray Marcos as provincial occurs again later in another document. There has been much controversy on the subject. Some say he was made provincial after his return from the first journey.

Next in order was the army master, for whom the expedition was destined to be his last adventure in the service of his country:

"Lope de Samaniego, maestre de campo, swore that he is taking sixteen or seventeen horses, two buckskin coats, one coat of mail with its accouterments, some native cuirasses and weapons, since his other belongings were destroyed by fire." One of the objects included in the "accouterments," a helmet, was to play a ghastly role in the final act of Samaniego's brave life.

"Don Pedro de Tovar, chief ensign, swore that he is taking thirteen horses, one coat of mail, and some cuirasses and other native accouterments and weapons.

"Don Lope de Gurrea [Urrea], five horses, native weapons, Castile armor, headpiece, and buckskin coat.

"Hernando de Alvarado, captain of artillery, four horses, one coat of mail with sleeves, and native weapons, and other native equipment and arms.

"Don Alonso Manrique, three horses, native weapons, Castilian weapons, headpiece, and buckskin coat.

"Juan Gallego, coat of mail with breeches, buckskin coat, crossbow and other Castilian and native weapons, and seven horses. . . ."

So the muster roll went on, providing interesting matter to its very end, where it listed one Juan de Zaldívar, who had been appointed by Coronado, in 1538, as regidor of Compostela, where the review was now being held.

The viceroy was pleased to learn that there appeared to be peace and good will among all the groups of Spaniards, and that, so far as could be seen, there was no jealousy or envy manifested because one man held higher rank or had more possessions than did another.

A zealous Christian, Don Antonio had no thought of closing the review without invoking the blessing of God, in the Holy Sacrifice of the Mass, upon the men and their great objective. An altar had been set up on the plain. Now Fray Antonio de Victoria, a friar, clothed in the sacred vestments, advanced to the foot of it and began the recitation of the prayers.

All the horsemen, including General Coronado, dismounted and knelt on the greensward, joining with the celebrant in the petitions for God's blessing on their undertaking. The young leader, bowing his proud head, prayed for his own safety and that of his men, and for the interests left behind; especially for his beloved Beatriz, whom he had folded in his strong arms but a short time before in an anguish of farewell.

Mendoza, too, joined in the prayer of the priest and of his young friend, Coronado, asking that success attend their undertaking and that his men be spared at the hands of the unholy ones who had put to death Estevan the Moor, and who would surely have meted out a like fate to Fray Marcos de Niza had the friar dared to penetrate within the walls of their city.

By God's grace and their own prowess, the viceroy believed the army would succeed, where Fray Marcos had failed in part. Strong and fearless soldiers of Spain would force open the way for the planting of the Cross of Christ, where now pagan sticks and feathers waved from the ground and ignorant superstitious natives fell down to worship tiny streams of water gurgling out of the arid earth.

When the Mass was finished, the viceroy advanced to meet his troops and addressed them, briefly.

"I well know the good will and high worth of each man among you," he began, while a solemn hush settled down over the shining ranks. "Because of this, I would like to make each man a captain in this army of New Spain. This I cannot do, as you understand. Even so, I have full confidence that you will obey your general, Don Francisco Vásquez de Coronado, in a spirit of loyalty and perfect submission.

"Great profit and advantage to ourselves are certain to result from this expedition. First of all, it is undertaken for the glory of God, then for the aggrandizement of Spain and of his Majesty the King. The conversion of the Indians will be most pleasing to the Divine Majesty, as well as to His servant, the Emperor, upon the earth. And we shall all share in many good things of temporal nature later on, as a result of our courage and spirit of sacrifice. This enterprise is first of all a crusade of the Cross, and as such it must reap success, no matter how grave are the obstacles that must be overcome on the way."

Mendoza beckoned to Fray Antonio de Victoria, who now came to his side. In his hand the friar bore the missal just used in the celebration of the Mass.

The viceroy explained that he desired each man in the ranks to come forward, individually, and swear fealty on the sacred book.

This was done. Each soldier, touching the missal in his turn, swore that he would be obedient to his general and to his captain in all things and in every circumstance that should arise during the expedition.

Coronado was then "solemnly proclaimed and sworn in as captain general of His Majesty's latest formal army of occupation."

The viceroy deemed it well to allow the men to rest awhile, after the long ceremonies of the day. He, therefore, ordered them to remain at Compostela that night, and start the following morning soon after daybreak.

The departure took place on the morning of February 23 — Monday — under a clear brilliant sky. As the signal to march was given by Mendoza, General Coronado's noble beast stepped proudly forward, followed by the horses of the captains according to the rank of each man.

The viceroy rode beside the general; he was to accompany the army for a couple of days' journey. The hopes of both men were unbounded, and they were shared by every Spaniard in the company.

Francisco Vásquez de Coronado said nothing to his chief about the burden he found very hard to bear. Hardships and perils beyond any he could reckon possibly awaited before Cíbola should be taken for God and Spain. These, however, would be light and bearable in comparison with the pain and loneliness engendered by separation from his dearly loved wife.

No commander in chief could reckon with that sentiment of a young man's heart.

DON FRANCISCO VÁSQUEZ DE CORONADO, general of the army of Nueva España, on his way to conquer the countries to the far north, was early to discover that great enterprises are ever fraught with difficulties and hazards. One cause of disturbance was soon to manifest itself.

The general was aware that the task of transporting their personal baggage would prove very burdensome and awkward to most of the men, long inured to idleness and luxurious living in the capital. Don Francisco had found it, too, somewhat disconcerting that he had been obliged to share in the expense of outfitting the army. Sixty thousand ducats had gone from his private fortune to add to Mendoza's pool — among the soldiers it was whispered that Coronado had probably drawn on the fortune of his wife to raise the money.

The horses were not well adapted for the adventure lying ahead. Most of them were overheavy as a result of being too well fed and too little exercised. Their movements were slow and they showed themselves little disposed to accomodate their pace to the feverish eagerness of their riders. Soon it became evident that every horseman must dismount in order that the beasts might be utilized as carriers for the baggage, since the foot soldiers were proceeding at a snail's pace under the heavy loads.

All now became foot soldiers. Their general was edified and relieved to find that no complaints were heard in their ranks. He would have been deemed a coward who quailed beneath this first proof. Coronado himself gave the example of fortitude by walking beside his mount, as did the other gentlemen in the ranks. His words of encouragement and commendation lent heart to the men, although it could hardly do the same for the horses.

Not only did the soldiers carry much of their baggage from this stage of the march on, but corn for the horses as well. Thus impeded, it proved no easy task to penetrate the thickets along the flat and uninteresting coastal stretch. When, however, these sturdy men saw their general willingly enduring the same hardships as themselves, they were convinced of his generosity and high purpose, and bore every inconvenience and difficulty without murmuring.

Coming to the Rio Grande de Santiago, named in honor of the illustrious patron of Spain, Saint James, the army was obliged to remain there for several days. At this point the sheep, less accustomed to hardships than the rest of the stock in the caravan, had to be lifted across the stream, otherwise they would have been swept away by the strong current.

The high-spirited general chafed a little at this delay. But the men were soon able to proceed without further hindrance across a long uneven tract of country, ridged with hills, and with the volcanic peaks of Sanganguey and Ceboruco shadowing the eastern horizon line. The spirits of all in the company mounted as they realized that every step was taking them nearer to the goal of their ambition.

The trail, considerably narrowed after leaving the Santiago, was fringed by the blue waters of the South Sea to westward, while above them towered the steep slopes of the Sierra Madre.

Soon the path became dissected crosswise by the alluvial valleys of small rivers, whose sources were in the mountains; tumbling over the sandy lagoons and marshes, they formed a picture not unpleasing to the eye. These rivers were the San Pedro, the Acaponeta, the Canas and the Baluarte. Beyond this, the army journeyed over lowlying swamp land, badly infested with mosquitoes. These pests occasioned no little misery to the soldiers, while the Indians did not appear to notice them. They settled down in thick swarms over their prey, and the Spaniards were kept busy striking at them continuously.

Often Coronado's thought strayed to the little friar, Marcos de Niza, who had passed this way not long before, blazing a trail for the army of New Spain to follow. Fray Marcos must have experienced similar discomforts on the tortuous way. A religious, and a priest, he was human; he had a body as well as a soul, and he, too, could suffer in both. The young leader thought that he would not have cared to make the journey to Cíbola unattended by a white man . . . that, possibly, was one difference between a man of God and a man of the world. Even so, Don Francisco did not envy Fray Marcos his vocation.

On the lower Acaponeta River the army came into a valley formerly inhabited by men of a cultivated race. Nuño de Guzmán had marched there with his men and raided the place, seizing sufficient provisions to supply his party for a long time. Later, a disastrous flood had taken all but the lives of the inhabitants; it had carried off their flat-roofed dwellings, filled with pottery of their own making, and all their other possessions. Then, too, various tribes in the near-by hills had descended upon the land until all but a few stragglers among the inhabitants withdrew, deserting their little coastal settlements. In addition to these misfortunes, the Indians coming from the hills for plunder had brought with them a dreadful pestilence which drove away or carried off by death many of the settlers.

Coronado and his followers found the few people remaining in the deserted place very antagonistic, and were glad to pass beyond it.

It was mid-March when the expedition reached a settlement on the Rio Presidio called Chametla. Guzmán had founded it, bestowing the beautiful name, Espíritu Santo, upon it. Now it was nearly empty of Spaniards, for the majority of them had gone to Peru, won by the dazzling fortunes of the Pizarros. Francisco Pizarro, the son of a swineherd, had accomplished seemingly incredible military achievements in the kingdom of the Inca princes; this he had done by the sheer force and purpose of his indomitable energy and determination. Don Francisco Vásquez de Coronado, a former courtier at the royal court of Spain, singled out as the favorite of the viceroy of Nueva España, and entrusted with a gigantic enterprise in a virgin country, was determined to achieve something of great importance, also. This was the conquest of the Seven Cities of Cíbola.

Lope de Samaniego, a veteran of the Guzmán expedition, a former member of the cabildo [the municipal council], and until recently warden of one of His Majesty's fortresses in Mexico, approached the general with a proposition.

"The food supply is very low, General," Samaniego said. "It seems we should send out a foraging party to replenish our stores. The Indian tribes in this vicinity are still rebellious, and we may experience some difficulty in bartering with them. But we must have food for the men and horses."

Coronado gave the desired permission. He was thinking that Samaniego was a fit instrument for any hazardous undertaking. The officer was fearless, obedient, devoted, and willing to do anything in his power to carry out a commission entrusted to him.

As the army master departed to gather a few picked men for the foray into the unfriendly hills, his leader looked with satisfaction upon the stalwart figure, striding from him into the camp. He could not possibly know that he looked for the last time into the living face of his friend.

The foraging party under the leadership of Samaniego soon came to the end of the clearing where the soldiers were lined up. The underbrush ahead was very dense. As they were endeavoring to break through this, a crossbowman in the group withdrew from his companions and entered one of the Indian villages. He did so in total disregard of the orders he had received, which were that all the men should remain together unless ordered to do otherwise by their leader.

At no time so far were any natives to be seen in the vicinity. The army master and his men, however, were not too certain of their immunity from harm or of the success of their enterprise, for the Indians were treacherous and, also, very shrewd in calculating their moves.

In a few moments a scream reached the ears of the party. The disobedient and unwary soldier who had proceeded into the village had been suddenly surrounded and taken by a number of natives, who darted out from ambush and attacked him.

Samaniego could hardly believe the evidence of his ears. Scanning his soldiers, in a flash he discovered the absence of the crossbowman. Angered that he had dared to disobey, but faithful to care for the interests of those entrusted to his charge, the officer called his men together and they hurried to the place of the conflict.

When they appeared on the scene the Indians had disappeared, having escaped to their hiding places as if by

magic. No one but the wounded Spaniard was in sight.
All seemed well.

Ordering several of the men to assist the victim of the
attack, Samaniego scouted a little to see if he could ascertain the direction in which the Indians had fled.

In an unfortunate moment, he raised the visor of his
helmet, that he might better observe the locality.

As he did so, an arrow whistled through the near-by
thicket and struck him in the eye. Passing thence through
his brain, it felled the brave soldier to the ground. Five
or six of Samaniego's men were likewise wounded by arrow darts, some to death.

Diego López, a former alderman from Seville, gathered
the living about him and together they made their retreat, bearing the dead in their arms. At a safe distance,
the bodies were temporarily interred in a field.

Dismayed and antagonized by the murder of their
faithful leader, some of Samaniego's men went back to
the Indian village, took prisoner and hanged to trees a
number of the natives who, they had reason to believe,
were implicated in the deed.

Into the astonished presence of Don Francisco Vásquez
the group of Spaniards returned, with the disconcerting
news. The general's face turned ashen. He had lost an
ally and servitor on whom he could count for any sacrifice. The army master had died in a hero's role — but that
was small comfort now to his general. The latter contem-
plated in bitterness of soul the helmet formerly worn by
the dead leader, which one of the men presented to him.
Confused thoughts ran through the young don's mind
. . . this was the first casualty of the expedition. Would it
be followed by others — perhaps by many others?

Coronado issued instructions for the ultimate disposition of his friend's body:

"When the time is ripe, we shall bear him back to the

chapel of Espíritu Santo, at Chametla, and there inter him as is fitting, with the rites of the Church. Later on I shall see to it that he is removed and taken to Compostela, where many of us who loved him can visit and pray at his tomb."

Trained as he was to confidence, courage and submission, Coronado found that his peace of mind was to be disrupted soon again.

Two horsemen now rode hurriedly into the camp. Their faces registered grave disquiet. They came from the north, and they bore news which was to still further test the mettle of Don Francisco and his captains.

In the previous autumn Viceroy Mendoza had sent two of his followers, Melchior Díaz and Juan de Zaldívar, with fifteen horsemen, from Culiacán, to try to explore the terrain covered by Fray Marcos de Niza in his journey northward, and if possible corroborate what the friar had reported concerning the lands he had visited. Now, returning from their quest, these men told a tale not greatly consoling to the general's ears.

Melchior Díaz acted as spokesman. He stated that with his companion officer and their men he had left Culiacán on November 17, 1539. The Indians beyond the Rio Petatlán were generous in supplying the party with food, despite an unfavorable harvest. Díaz had ensured this kind treatment by sending, in advance of his coming, a wooden cross; this was to signify that his intentions were peaceful.

The Indians received this cross with respect and gratification. When Díaz arrived in their midst, he was treated munificently and provided with every necessity for himself and his men.

The party had gone on for a hundred leagues. Midwinter set in and the cold and frost rendered the journey very difficult. Yet they continued until they came to a place called Chichilticalli, a town situated near the Gila River.

Here they stopped, subdued and somewhat intimidated by the trials they had suffered. A number of their Indian allies had frozen to death along the way, because their meager garments proved wholly insufficient to keep warmth and life in their bodies. Wisely, Díaz determined to turn back at this point.

He described Cíbola as he had learned about it. The Indians of Chichilticalli, in fact, spoke of it quite willingly. They stated that some of them had lived there for a period of from fifteen to twenty years. They confirmed much of what Fray Marcos de Niza had said about it — for instance, that the houses of Cíbola were stone, plastered with mud; that they were three and four stories in height and had loopholes for defense in the outer walls. The Chichilticalli Indians also said that when the people of Cíbola went forth to do battle they wore cowhide jackets; that when they were at peace they sang and danced and by way of accompaniment played the flute.

Díaz had made careful inquiries as to the purported riches of Cíbola, since this was the point that most deeply interested the Spaniards.

In this regard, however, the Indians gave testimony which was very disconcerting to the white men. They stated that there was no gold there, or other precious metal. There were turquoises, but only a few of these.

The natives who lived just south of Chichilticalli had proved decidedly hostile to Díaz and his party. Not only did they extend no welcome to them, but they had shown extreme dissatisfaction at their presence.

Díaz was told, too, of the very disagreeable dictum issuing from Cíbola. For the natives of that place threatened that if the "Christians" persisted in advancing into their midst, they would be slaughtered as if they were so many wild beasts. The relics of Estevan the Moor testified to the mortality of the strangers — they were not gods, but men, whose bodies could be torn by arrow points and whose flesh could be cut piecemeal and divided among the native chiefs.

Coronado was sorely disturbed by this account. Into his thoughts came the memory of his beloved wife, Doña Beatriz. Was any venture, no matter what reward it promised, worth the relinquishing of one hour of her sweet company? And might not he, as well as Samaniego the dead army master, suffer some evil fate before he should be able to return to her side?

The general determined to keep this bad news from his men, if it was possible to do so. He knew that everything depended upon maintaining them in a contented and optimistic frame of mind.

Calling to him Fray Marcos de Niza, who had rejoined the expedition along the way, Coronado said to him:

"Father, I would like you to go among my men and tell them about the things you saw on your recent journey. Tell them, especially, about the Seven Cities, as you saw them from a distance. Assure them that they will be well rewarded if they persevere in their present good will, in the face of all difficulties that may present themselves. I shall be most grateful to you for doing us this new service."

Fray Marcos was happy to comply with the request. His face shone with ardor and trust as he mingled with the soldiers, telling them over and over again of his wonderful experience in the north; promising them that they would soon feast their eyes on many good things and enjoy rich rewards in return for their confidence in their general. Then all the hardships and disappointments of the journey would be wholly forgotten and they would enjoy happiness unalloyed.

The stern countenances of the men gradually cleared, and assumed a more cheerful aspect. Grim looks on the part of those who were less hopeful gave way to an expression of confidence and they advanced no further argument against Cíbola, believing that the good Franciscan spoke with true knowledge when he promised them all good things at the end of their journey.

The march was resumed, with occasional detours into the interior for gathering provisions. At vespers of Easter the army came within two leagues of the Spanish outpost of Culiacán.

THE TOWNSPEOPLE of San Miguel were engaged in the exercises of the Easter festival when the army arrived in their midst. They did not choose to be disturbed by armed forces at this hallowed time. A little group of them came out to meet the advancing ranks. They had a request to proffer to General Coronado. It was that he would consent to remain outside the gates of the town until the day after the feast. Also, they stated, they wished to have sufficient time to prepare fittingly for the reception of the courageous soldiers of the king. They expressed their desire to put to the test their own martial abilities, and suggested that the general would arrange for a sham fight, to be staged between his men and the Spaniards within the fortress.

Coronado agreed to all these propositions. With his men he remained outside the town until the morning of Easter Monday. On that day, soon after dawn, they approached to meet the inhabitants. Both forces met in a clearing, with horsemen and soldiers drawn up as if ready for a skirmish with an enemy.

The townspeople made a brave showing of their seven pieces of field artillery, as the mock skirmish began. After the artillery of both sides was discharged, the townspeople retreated, as if put to rout by a superior force.

At the conclusion of this demonstration, Don Francisco Vásquez de Coronado rode into the town, his men following. There they received all possible courtesy and attention.

Weary, and covered with sweat and dust as a result of their experiences up to this time, the army availed themselves of the opportunity to refresh themselves and enjoy the hospitality extended to them without stint. They remained at San Miguel for several weeks, generously treated by the people, who, no doubt, hoped to be well recompensed for their kindness when the visitors should return from Cíbola, laden with rich spoils.

Following out Mendoza's orders, Coronado left a captain and ally in the town, a Spaniard named Fernandarias Saabedra. When the army finally departed, lustily cheered by the townspeople, their six hundred or more pack animals carried supplies sufficient to last for a long period.

The gallant general rode ahead of the main body. With him were fifty horsemen, a small band of foot soldiers, and most of the Indian allies. In command of the soldiers who were to follow later on he left Don Tristán de Arellano as his lieutenant.

Coronado's peace of mind had suffered considerably ever since the untimely death of his trusted friend and army master, Samaniego. An incident which occurred shortly before the march from San Miguel had vexed and disturbed him to the point of extreme anger.

A young soldier named Truxillo stated that, as he was taking a bath in the river, he had seen a vision and received a startling communication. The devil, he affirmed, appeared to him and told him that if he, Truxillo, would kill his general, he could marry Coronado's beautiful wife, Doña Beatriz, and that great wealth and luxury would be his.

Coronado placed no credence in the audacious tale, yet it shook him to the very depths. He was sorely displeased that the name of his beloved wife should rest lightly in the heart and on the lips of the soldier. He ordered Truxillo to remain behind in the town. This order did not appear to distress the youth, which fact led his companions to think that he had not been eager to go on to Cíbola, possibly fearful of the perils to be met with on the way, and so manufactured the tale.

Glancing a few paces behind, the general brightened as his gaze rested on the gray robes and white cordeliers of the spiritual sons of Saint Francis of Assisi. Of the three friars enrolled in the expedition, but two were present. Fray Antonio Victoria, a regular friar, who could celebrate Mass for the men, had suffered a broken leg in a fall on the third day after the army left the valley of Culiacán. Taken back to camp, he had remained there, to the great joy of the soldiers who were to wait in that place until Coronado should send for them to rejoin him.

The presence of the servants of Christ brought peace and tranquillity to the heart of Don Francisco. Recalling Truxillo and his "vision," the young don smiled indulgently and forgave the soldier his impertinence.

It was Melchior Díaz who recalled the gentle Beatriz to Coronado's mind in even more vivid manner by a suggestion he made at this time. Coming up to his chief before the army had fairly left Culiacán behind, he said to him:

"General, I will send two or three of these comely Indian women back to Mexico, where they may serve Doña Beatriz, if you will. It seems they could be useful in that capacity. And, of course, it would not be difficult to win them to the faith. What does Your Excellency think of my proposition?"

Don Francisco did not think too highly of it.

"The distance back to Mexico is too great. The trip would be very hard on the women," he responded.

When Díaz persisted in his request, the general promised to think the matter over and give his decision later.

In a retired spot, Don Francisco knelt at the feet of one of the friars, and, after making his confession, asked his advice in regard to Díaz' proposition.

His confessor thought well of it. He said to his penitent: "Assuredly, have the women sent back. At home, and in the company of Doña Beatriz, they will most certainly become Christians, and have an opportunity to increase in the knowledge of God and of holy things. If they remain here, they will continue in their heathen customs — shameful, many of these customs are, as Your Excellency must have noticed."

Schooled to act readily on religious counsel, Don Francisco sought out Melchior Díaz and told him that he might do as he wished. So, two of the Indian women were sent back under escort to the lady Beatriz.

Four years later, the sending of these native women to the capital of Nueva España was to be charged against Coronado as an unlawful act. This happened as a result of the investigation of his administration as governor of Nueva Galicia. The particular charge was refuted, although other allegations of maladministration were sustained.

The general traveled somewhat lightly equipped, for he wished to make as much speed as possible. He had previously ascertained that the route over which the army now marched was uninhabited and without provision of any kind.

In all the hitherto inhabited sections, the gentle presence and address of Fray Marcos de Niza had not been forgotten by the Indians along Coronado's route. Because of this, the general was welcomed and permitted to go on his way without molestation of any kind. These natives had previously known Melchior Díaz and Juan de

Saldívar, sent north to try to corroborate the story told by Fray Marcos after the latter's return from Cíbola. All this was very heartening to Don Francisco, whose hopes ascended at every stage of the march, despite the disturbances already encountered.

The general had started from San Miguel with his picked army on April 22. Spring was on the decline when he rode jubilantly into Petatlán, the little village of the grass mats. He and his men had now traveled over eighty miles of their journey.

The natives of this small settlement did not tempt fate by refusing to provide comforts for the white men. They had learned a hard lesson at the hands of Spanish raiders coming from the south and were unwilling to risk further trouble, but the army did not tarry in this pleasant spot. Leaving the sea still farther behind, they marched through a bleak, dreary waste of desert that was to test their mettle to the breaking point.

Blinding heat lay upon the dull red soil, and the thorny flutings of the cactus, upright and rigid, seemed to defy the intruders as they passed slowly on their way. Everything blazed, most of all the gilded armor of the general, which seemed to be the focus of it all. The horses began to drag their hoofs, often stumbling and slipping in the soft sand, to be encouraged and helped to their feet by their dispirited masters. The men afforded themselves the scant physical comfort provided by the straggling tunas, and the occasional mesquites and pitahayas found along the way.

So three days of this misery passed. Better things were now in store. The army crossed the Rio Sinaloa, foaming down from lofty sierras, refreshing mind and eye alike as it provided a welcome contrast to the thorny wastes left behind.

The general believed that some thirty leagues beyond,

traces of Fray Marcos' wonderful country of gold and precious gems would appear. Therefore, he ordered Díaz to take with him a dozen horsemen, lightly equipped, and, making double marches, explore the country to the right of the trail. Díaz was ordered to meet him, later, at the junction of the Rio Mayo and the Arroyo de los Cedros, the latter so called because of the many Mexican trees lining its banks. Both rivers entered the territory from the north.

When Díaz returned, it was to bring to his general a very discouraging report. That intrepid scout, traveling up the Mayo through exceedingly rough mountain territory, had seen no signs of either food or gold. He reported the land to be very unfertile, having only a few poor villages of twenty to thirty huts apiece. An Indian whom he met on the route said that he knew of no gold ornaments, such as those mentioned by Fray Marcos, to be found in the vicinity.

Some part of this report seeped through the ranks of the soldiers, although Coronado tried to prevent it. Noting that the men were becoming somewhat disturbed as a result of these rumors, he endeavored to arouse their courage and optimism.

"Our noble viceroy told me at the outset that this part of our march would be unproductive and lacking in every comfort," he said. "But he also remarked that we must devote all our energies to the discovery and conquest of the Seven Cities and the other provinces of which we have heard. Let us proceed fearlessly, looking for the great reward of our sacrifices later on."

The exhortation, so necessary at the moment, bore some fruit. However, the general himself was not too hopeful, since in many places the roads were so rough that it was necessary to stop and repair them, or even to build new ones, before going on. All the men were impatient over the enforced delay, which added greatly to the difficulties and burdens of the expedition. They realized, too, that these stops necessitated the consumption of the usual amount of food, while, at the same time, no advance was made.

Traversing, finally, the headwaters of the Cedros and the swiftly flowing Rio Chico, the party came to the Rio Yaqui. Here Coronado received a report on the condition of his livestock. As a result of it, he decided to leave behind four horsemen in charge of twenty-four lambs and four wethers, all of whose hoofs had come off in the toilsome climb over the mountains. The rest had died as a result of the hardships they were forced to endure. Coronado issued instructions to the effect that these lambs and wethers were to be brought later to Cíbola by the horsemen.

This circumstance did not elevate the jaded spirits of the men, for it betokened a scarcity of provisions in the near future. Coronado himself was not worried over the situation; he had faith in the loyalty of his men, a faith that eventually proved to be fully justified.

Leaving the Yaqui behind, the party took a turn to the left. Soon they arrived at a little Indian village of straw huts. These Indians had a good supply of corn, beans and melons, which they were quite willing to share with the strangers. When they were strengthened by their fill of food and had something to carry away with them, the men resumed the journey. On the twenty-sixth day of May they entered the famed valley of Corazones, which Cabeza de Vaca had visited.

Here, in an irrigation arroyo, where the climate was warm and agreeable, a group of Opata Indians lived in huts fashioned from poles, erected in the shape of ovens and covered with mats. They dressed in deerskin, and cultivated maize, beans and calabashes in abundance.

The general's keen eyes observed that extensive planted fields stretched away on every side, and that there were more Indians in the place than in any he had previously visited.

. However, he was greatly disappointed to find that the Opatas had nothing to share with his men, for the year's harvest had not been successful. They had no more than sufficient provisions to supply their own needs. The present crop of maize was not yet ripe, and the Opatas had no supplies of corn. They told the general that in Sonora, a valley lying in his path, the natives cultivated and raised corn.

Although the Spaniards were not cheered by this report, they remained several days at Corazones. Coronado observed that the sea took a turn to westward directly opposite the town. He learned that the ship sent by Viceroy Mendoza to find the port of Chichilticalli had been sighted, but no one knew more of it. Coronado had left a full supply of food at Culiacán for the men on shipboard, so that he felt no anxiety on that score.

The army, about to push on from the Valley of the Hearts, was slightly smaller than when it had reached there. A group of Negroes and Indians had deserted the expedition, discouraged by the trials they had borne. Ten or twelve of the horses, unable to bear the strain of dragging heavy burdens over rough country, and having little to eat, had died. The young don was certain that these trials were slight in comparison with others that lay ahead.

Once more he determined to send Díaz on a scouting mission. His objective was, if possible, to find food. He believed that he would be successful in the quest, since he relied on the assurance given him at Corazones that there was plenty of food ahead, in the Sonora Valley. Díaz was instructed to barter with the Sonora Indians and carry back to the army what provisions he could obtain.

For this purpose Díaz took with him certain commodities which he was prepared to offer in exchange for food. He was anxious to supply the necessities of life to the friendly Indian allies and others who, having lost their animals on the trip, had not been able to carry the provisions given them at Culiacán.

Only a little maize was obtained by this trading. It was divided among the soldiers and the Indians. For the time being it sufficed to quiet their pangs of hunger.

As they had come to visit Fray Marcos de Niza, so now some Indians from the coast sought out Coronado. They informed him that a wild and barbarous tribe lived in that region. These Indians were the savage Seris, some of whose emissaries had elected to follow Fray Marcos to Cíbola.

His native guests told the general that he was then five miles from the sea, though actually the distance was much greater.

Before departing from Corazones, Coronado, believing it a suitable spot for a Spanish settlement, gave orders that one should be established there. This town, which was subsequently moved to two other locations in succession, was named the Villa de San Gerónimo de los Corazones. Both its later locations were farther up the stream.

Through a small natural gateway the army passed into the land of Sonora. Proceeding amidst high sierras and through deep gorges, often both men and beasts recoiled as some sinister serpent glided too near for comfort, or some huge wild bird swooped down before their very noses and eyes, its wings making a great rushing sound.

Fifteen miles across the wide canyon of the Sonora the

party came into the Suya Valley, where the last Opata town south of the Cananea plain was located.

General Coronado was interested and, perhaps, a little alarmed to receive information at this point about a certain deadly poison kept by these Indians to effect the destruction of their enemies. It was said to be the worst that could be conceived, and came from the sap of a tree like the lentisk, growing among broken shale and in arid and unproductive soil. It was the sap of the "Poisonous Tree," of which Fray Marcos de Niza had learned during his earlier journey.

It appeared that the customs followed by the Indians in this locality resembled those which, so the white men had heard, prevailed in Cíbola. Public proclamations were made to the people, not, however, from the rooftops, as in Cíbola, but from the tops of mounds erected for the purpose. In this way the people received instructions as to what they must do.

There seemed to be plenty of food in the place, but the army moved quickly forward. As they continued on the march, they traveled for four days over grassy plains between high mountain peaks. A stream of water flowed northward through the land.

Every little contribution of food made by the friendly Indians along the route was gratefully accepted by the Spaniards. It consisted mainly of small quantities of roasted maguey and pitahaya fruit growing on the property of the natives living along the river banks.

This brief pleasant stage of the journey soon led into harsher paths. Again the general and his followers traversed a dry tract of uninhabited wasteland. As Fray Marcos de Niza had experienced, in this land of clear dry air it was easy for the eye to build up, in the distance, imaginary palaces, golden and opalescent, and lovely to behold. The spirits of the men soared whenever they glimpsed such a phantasm of beauty, for it recalled to their minds all they had heard about Cíbola and its queenly cities.

Fortunately there was sufficient water in the place to slake the thirst of the men. Now, down a low, but still running stream, they proceeded a two days' journey. Branching to the right, and advancing to the foot of a mountain chain, they heard of the settlement called Chichilticalli. It was this settlement which just now they were most anxious to reach.

Their desire was fulfilled when the mountains were crossed and they came upon another pleasant river, this one deep, and fringed with cool green rushes.

Men and horses refreshed themselves in the stream. Then they examined with keenest interest — and no small chagrin — the solitary house in the place, a dilapidated roofless structure, whose mud walls, streaked with ocher-colored paint, constituted the sole relic of some tribe once living there.

Impatiently, some of the soldiers questioned Fray Marcos de Niza, who was of the party, about this country. He reported that it was the location closest to the sea. Yet, after investigation, it had been ascertained that the speediest Indian runner required full ten days to reach the coast.

Harsh words and looks were directed at the friar, and the soldiers muttered together. Many of them now began to shun his presence and Coronado himself remained aloof from him. Perhaps, however, the general realized that Fray Marcos' notes, made on his journey of the previous year, were meager and sketchy, due to the strain of the adventure and the many embarrassments encountered from its beginning to its end. In writing the account later, was it not possible that he had confused the

location of Cíbola with the region where first the realization came to him that he was far inland?

The surliness and aloofness of the men of the army
were hard for Fray Marcos to bear. Yet his Franciscan
courtesy did not forsake him when he met some of those
who treated him contumeliously. Saluting them with the
kindliness and cheerful spirit of his Seraphic Father, he
said:

"The Lord give thee peace!"

XX

EVEN THE THOUGHT of the glittering treasure they hoped to acquire in Cíbola, by force of arms if by no other means, could not distract the minds of the soldiers so as to take from them the realization that they were half famished and that food was the most desirable boon at the present time.

For two days they remained at Chichilticalli, looking eagerly down one of the two small branches of the Gila River, which flowed in the direction of the Seven Cities. The delay did not add to their comfort or peace of mind and they waited impatiently for Coronado to give the signal to resume the march.

The gaunt red-roofed house which Fray Marcos de Niza had seen when he reached that point in his northern journey of the previous year loomed like a ghostly phantom on the horizon. The Spaniards found no consolation in it, for it had evidently been despoiled by the Indians of that region, the most savage tribe they had so far encountered. These natives made their dwellings in occasional clusters of tiny huts and lived by the hunt. It appeared that they had no permanent habitations.

Consoling in some small measure to the army was the fact that the country was liberally supplied with nuts. There were many oak trees, bearing sweet acorns and panonas; these produced a fruit similar to that from which coriander preserves were made. This fruit, however, when dried, was as sweet as sugar and could not be eaten in that condition in any quantity.

Wandering about during their brief stay in the place, the soldiers discovered watercress growing in some of the springs. They cut down branches of the pennyroyal and wild majoram, which abounded, and, fishing in the rivers of the *desplobado*, caught some barbles and picones — small fish resembling the catfish and trout. Frequently they espied gray lions in the distance.

Coronado was told that from Chichilticalli the land rose gradually until Cíbola was reached. This news was not too heartening, for it meant additional strain in the long marches across difficult terrain.

Ahead lay another wilderness, almost without trace of any living thing. Over this dreary tract the army must pass if the goal of its burning ambition was to be realized. With mouths gritty from the desert sand, and with faces blistered and burned by the hot dry winds, the men trudged onward, not forgetting to voice menacing complaints in regard to their lot in the hearing of Fray Marcos de Niza.

The friar walked meekly in the caravan, experiencing a twofold misery of which the physical part was by far less burdensome. He now found himself a pariah, unwanted and unhonored, even shunned by the disillusioned soldiers, whose disappointment was stamped in every line of their haggard faces. The fatigues and hardships of his first journey to Cíbola had told on the sturdy little friar, and now his ardent spirit was heavily weighted down with pain. Fearless bold adventurers, despite the fact that many of them represented the first blood of Spain, the men did not hesitate to show unmitigated contempt for him and even to lay the blame for all their present miseries at his door. Coronado was silent, wondering, perhaps, if the coveted prize was to fall far short of his cherished expectations and desires.

Passing next through a mountainous tract, which was entered on Saint John's Eve, June 23, the column of soldiers and Indians wound along in a land of silence and loneliness. The proud feather in the young general's helmet drooped low, as, his head bent over his horse's neck, he allowed his stiff body to relax in a different posture.

Following a custom he had adopted, very prudently, at the start of the expedition, Coronado now decided to send a party ahead to explore the territory and prepare the way for the army to follow. He selected his newly appointed maestro de camp, Don García López de Cárdenas, to head a group of fifteen horsemen, and ordered him to proceed a day's journey and ascertain the nature of the country beyond. Coronado knew that the viceroy had found Cárdenas very reliable, and he had no fear in entrusting such a commission to him.

The report brought back by the scout was not heartening. He and his men found the land very rough, indeed, almost impassible for about thirty leagues. They had met four Indians on the banks of the Rio Vermejo. These natives intimated that they were anxious to establish peace with the white men; they stated that they were messengers, sent by the rulers of Cíbola, to welcome them.

Cárdenas presented them with a cross, which they received with evident pleasure and good will. They then promised that food would be provided for the army.

The maestro de camp told them of Coronado's coming, assuring them that they need have no fear of him since he came in the name of his great lord, to help and defend the people of Cíbola.

The officer presented the four Indians, also, with some

small cloaks, which, like the cross, appeared to be very acceptable.

The experienced Cárdenas did not wholly credit the assurances of these Indians and determined to warn his general of what he believed was their real intention — to get information about the white men in order to prepare to resist them.

When Coronado heard the report, he shared in the maestro's suspicions. The scout was ordered to return with a guard to the spot where he had met the natives, and hold any narrow passes where they might be lying in ambush.

The army then proceeded to march toward the Seven Cities.

They found the passage very rough, as Cárdenas had said it was. However, their courage was strengthened by the realization that they were now not far from their goal. They were amply repaid for their fortitude when they entered a cool verdant country, through which several small rivers flowed.

The first of these rivers, crossed after leaving the Gila behind, was the Gila Bonito. This river the Spaniards renamed the San Juan, because the advance party had come up to it on the eve of Saint John's feast. The next good-sized stream was reached two days later. This was the Salada, or Salt River; it was renamed the Rio de las Balsas, because the men crossed it in little rafts called *balsas*. After two more days they came to a stream which they christened the Rio de las Barrancas, or the River of Ravines, a small stream in the White Mountains [perhaps an upper branch of the Rio Chiquito]. Two days further they reached the Chiquito proper.

Coronado himself gave the name to the last-mentioned river. Because a goodly amount of flax grew on its banks, he called it Rio de Lino.

Another two days' march beyond this point brought them to the river of Cíbola. Its waters, a dull muddy red, suggested the title, Rio Vermejo, Red River.

The general was gravely concerned over the food problem, never far removed from his calculations. In all, scarcely two bushels of maize remained on hand. The numbers of the Mexican Indian allies was greatly diminished, due to deaths from starvation and cold; those who now dragged themselves onward were extremely weak as a result of the lack of proper nourishment and clothing.

On approaching Cíbola, Coronado sent Don Pedro de Tovar and Melchior Díaz to bring to him Indians from a group living near a lake, to gather information and also secure an interpreter from them. The general explained to these natives, through an interpreter he had brought from the Corazones Valley, that he came in the name of His Majesty, to place them under his dominion and to bring them to the knowledge of the true God. He told them that they should become Christians, and that no harm would be done them in their persons or properties, provided that they submitted peacefully to the obedience of His Majesty. When the messengers returned to their people, Coronado sent two Mexican Indians with them, bearing a cross, an emblem of peace, in their hands. As it transpired, the Indians of that pueblo did not want peace.

The walls of Cíbola must be stormed. The failure of the messengers with the cross to placate the natives, and the recollection of Estevan's fate assured Coronado of this necessity. But how was this to be successfully accomplished, since the Spanish soldiers were far below the peak of physical prowess? Less than one hundred of them, with the small group of their allies, would hardly present an imposing battle front to the eyes of the hostile people of Cíbola.

The general was well aware that they expected his coming, that, in fact, they were awaiting him even before Cárdenas met the party of four during his scouting trip. Cárdenas had already experienced trouble, as was anticipated. Returning to the spot where the four natives had assured him of the friendliness of their people toward the newcomers, he discovered a certain dangerous spot where enemies could very well lurk in hiding without being seen, and easily launch an attack.

The maestro de camp with his men took possession of the place. Not too soon. For, when night fell, a band of natives appeared. Finding the group in possession, they made an unsuccessful attempt to overcome them. They were beaten back and forced to retreat. One of their number sounded a horn as a signal to his companions to withdraw; possibly, also, to inform the others of his tribe, at a little distance, of the fact that the white men had repulsed them.

Cárdenas was not edified to find that at the first sign of trouble, several of the less experienced soldiers in his band were badly frightened, and in their alarm, put the saddles on their horses hind side before.

General Coronado had good reason to expect more serious trouble after this beginning. When another night fell, he scanned the horizon for signal fires. He was not mistaken in thinking they would appear. Soon they flamed up from every hilltop, making the sky a lurid red. With murky smoke rising from their midst, they seemed to portend a grim encounter on the morrow.

The Indians were not correct in thinking that the white men were intent solely on avenging the death of Estevan the Moor. Coronado's thought at this time was not even of gold and silver and precious stones, but of food for his men and horses. This must be secured if all were not to perish of starvation in a short time. Momentarily it was becoming apparent that the Indian allies were the weakest of all, and that some of them would expire if forced to go without food for even one more day.

At last dawn broke. The general and his army, drawn up a short distance outside the walls of Hawikuh, the first city of Cíbola, looked upon the pueblos which had been so long the object of their fondest dreams. The day was Wednesday, the seventh of July, the year, 1540. Before the sun should set a great conflict was to be staged on that spot.

However, the thought of the coming conflict completely left the minds of all the Spaniards in a realization that brought acute sorrow, disappointment, even rage to their breasts. . . .

Hawikuh rose up, an unimposing jumble of round flat-roofed dwellings, three and four stories high, but in no way distinguished as they stood out in ragged silhouette against the irrigated fields to southward.

For a few moments there was no sound in the ranks, but a deadly hush settled over them. The Indian allies alone appeared indifferent and disinterested in the discovery.

Then, upon the quiet air, broke frightful sounds; the curses of bold hardy men who had sacrificed everything dear to them to follow a mirage; who, having come up to their goal, weary in brain and limb, enervated by heat and cold, by hunger and thirst, by pains in stomach and head and limb, found themselves the victims of a delusion, a dream never to be fulfilled.

Before their startled gaze rose up, not a queenly city, gleaming bright and beautiful in the morning sun, and inviting them to enter and avail themselves of its delights, but a poor Indian village, whose sole gems consisted of an occasional cluster of mediocre turquoises fastened in the doors of the houses nearest to the walls.

The curses grew louder, more vehement, as the men of the army realized more fully that their quest for gold and other precious loot was in vain. These unholy imprecations were hurled at Fray Marcos de Niza, who, standing apart, his countenance as gray as his robe and his eyes suffused with unshed tears, found himself the center of a storm of abuse. So fierce and terrible were the invectives hurled against him that Pedro de Castañeda, the historian of the expedition, writing of the affair years later, said: "I pray God to protect him from them."

Through the tortured brain of the friar a torrent of tumultuous thoughts ran swiftly. There was the remembrance of the joy and confidence that had inundated his soul at the first thought of the beautiful commission entrusted to him by the viceroy. He recalled the setting out, with God's blessing, on the road to the Seven Cities; the consistent reports of the wealth and loveliness of those cities all along the difficult and perilous route; Estevan's repeated assurances, sent to him from a distance northward, that everything told about the cities was true; the tragic ending of the adventure, in sight of the golden settlements, yet too far off for his eyes to be able to distinguish them clearly. . . .

Fray Marcos de Niza had believed the testimony of the many Indians whom he met on the journey. He had believed what he took to be the unquestionable evidence of his own eyes, although those tired eyes had deceived him. It was the atmospheric condition in that land of clear dry air which had erected a dazzling spectacle before him, as if to corroborate all he had been told, insistently, unfailingly, on every hand, regarding the Seven Golden Cities.

Now they proved to be no more substantial than an empty mirage, the result of a transfiguring sunset glory in that strange climate, but also of his own strained imagination and harassed brain, together with a vision enfeebled by hardship and lack of food.

Surely, death at the hands of those who had so swiftly dispatched the Moor would have been preferable to this anguish and torment of mind and soul. Perhaps Fray Marcos de Niza wished that he had gone forward, in the face of danger, and tested the fair vision — yet the viceroy had forbidden him needlessly to expose his life to danger.

As the tortured friar tried to formulate words of prayer, they seemed glued to his lips and would not come forth. Not even the consoling figure of his beloved father, Saint Francis, was there to comfort him in his hour of need . . . Francis, who had warned his sons of circumstances like this, which should arise, which must arise in the life of everyone who attempted great deeds for God.

Deeply wounded in spirit and disappointed by the discovery of the true status of Cíbola, Coronado was yet swift to act. He sent Cárdenas, with his secretary, Hernando Bermejo, who was also notary of the expedition, a little way ahead with a band of horsemen to treat with the Indians and tell them that the white men did not come to do them harm, but to defend them in the name of their lord, the Emperor.

The natives of Cíbola were intelligent — as they listened to the message, relayed through an interpreter, they might well have wondered just why the intruders thought the people of the pueblo stood in need of defense.

Fray Marcos de Niza was not invited to go on this commission with his brethren. Disgraced and discredited, he watched them as they advanced to enter the pueblo he himself would never enter.

XXI

HIS FORCES now united with Cárdenas and his little band of soldiers, General Coronado surveyed with practised eye the scene before him.

From various points within the pueblo of Hawikuh smoke was rising into a cloudless sky. The general had no doubt that the Indians had kindled fires, so that the view inside the walls might be cut off as far as possible.

The shrill notes of a horn now broke on the air. It seemed to be the signal for preparations to attack the white men, who had come to disturb the even tenor of primitive lives, possibly, the natives thought, to kill them.

Summoning Fray Luís to his side, the general said to the friar:

"You, Father, will please go forward with Don García López [Cárdenas] and Bermejo. Bermejo will read the proclamation of His Majesty to the people of Cíbola." As he spoke, Coronado handed a parchment to the notary.

Watching the three men walking toward the walls of the pueblo, the general decided that he, too, would attend the ceremony. Ordering a group of mounted men to follow him, and leaving instructions for the army to move on behind, he hastened to overtake the friar and his companions.

The general was somewhat dismayed to see at least

three hundred Indians coming toward them. They carried bows and arrows, and shields, and their appearance betokened grim determination to rout the invaders at any cost.

The formal demands contained in His Majesty's parchment, couched in faultless Castilian and transmitted to the Indians by the interpreter, failed to make any impression whatsoever. Three times Coronado and his aids endeavored to treat peaceably with the brown men. They refused to be influenced. In token of their good intentions the Spaniards even laid down their arms of warfare. This gesture, also, had no effect on the determined people of the pueblo. Although they had never seen either white men or horses before, and held the belief that the latter ate human beings, they refused to parley with the enemy.

"General, give us permission to open the attack!" Coronado's captains pleaded.

The general did not immediately accede to their request.

"We ought not to molest these people," he answered. "As yet they have done us no harm, and they are a comparatively small group when we consider that they have only native weapons to sustain their charge."

The Indians now began to send arrows in the direction of the Spaniards. Some of the horses were wounded and fell to the earth.

Seeing Fray Luís falter and sway to one side, Coronado sprang to his aid.

"You are hurt, Father!" he cried. "This is sufficient! We tarry no longer!"

The general quickly sought permission from the friars to open the attack, that it might be countenanced by the Church. This was readily granted, for the natives were inflicting many injuries on the white men with their well-directed arrows. Noting that the enemy had hesitated before returning their volley, they had grown audacious and fearless.

Ten or twelve Indians fell, mortally wounded, during the encounter which followed. The rest ran away in all directions, some into the pueblo, others in whatsoever path seemed best suited to escape.

Coronado determined to try to win over those who had taken refuge within the walls. At this turn of affairs, Fray Marcos de Niza appeared on the scene.

Fray Marcos was still suffering bitterly from the rude treatment accorded him by the soldiers, as well as from the overthrow of his cherished dream. Knowing that the general blamed him sorely for presenting a picture of Cíbola far from the reality, although his own conscience absolved him from all blame in the matter, yet he did not shrink from facing Don Francisco Coronado. He was consoled when Coronado addressed him with some show of kindness.

After acquainting the friar with all that had occurred outside the walls of Cíbola, the general asked him what he should do next.

Fray Marcos answered:

"Take your shields and go after them!"

The Spanish leader needed no urging to induce him to follow the advice. A brave man, anxious to do his part, the thought of his starving troops was uppermost in his mind. It nerved his heart and hand as, riding up to the walls with several of his captains, he launched a brisk attack on the Indians within. He then ordered the harquebusiers and crossbowmen to attack. The objective was to drive the enemy back, so that they could fire no more arrows into the Spanish ranks.

The harquebusiers and the crossbowmen were only too willing to obey their general, for the pangs of hunger were gnawing at their vital organs.

Unfortunately, their efforts proved to be puny. The musketeers could hardly stand on their legs sufficiently long to aim and fire, so weakened were they by the hardships and privations of the journey to Cíbola. Also, the strings of the crossbowmen, rotted by the fierce rays of desert suns, broke when put to the test.

The natives were quick to take advantage of this situation. From the top of the walls they continued their arrow shots and succeeded in wounding many of the Spaniards. Don Pedro de Tovar, the maestre de campo; Hernando de Alvarado, and the infantry captain, Pablo de Melgosa, were badly bruised by stones hurled down upon them. Fortunately, they were not seriously wounded. Gómez Suárez suffered an arrow wound in the arm, and a Spaniard named Torres was similarly wounded in the face. Two of the foot soldiers received slight arrow wounds.

Don Francisco de Coronado had not reckoned on one adverse circumstance in connection with his leadership of the expedition. This was that his rank was only too evident from the glittering mail which covered his body, as well as from the gilded helmet, adorned with plumes, which protected his head. These distinguishing marks now caused him to become the main objective of the efforts of the natives.

Detaching himself from the others, the general, gaining entrance to the pueblo, found himself in a narrow street. It seemed deserted so that he dared to proceed a short distance to a ladder which rested against the wall of a near-by house. He had scaled partway up this ladder, in the hope of gaining the roof and from that vantage directing his men below, when he was struck by a shower of stones, hurled upon him by the watchful Indians.

Coronado fell to the ground. However, unhurt, he decided to make a second attempt to accomplish his purpose.

This proved to be as useless and disastrous as the first. Again, a shower of stones brought him low. The Indians, believing him dead, made no further attempt to wound him, but turned their attention elsewhere.

Knocked senseless, the intrepid leader did not know that, as he struck the ground, someone sprang forward and prostrated himself over his inert body, so that, in the event of another onslaught, no arrow or stone should reach him. Missing his general, the faithful Don García López de Cárdenas had gone in search of him. He found Coronado, unconscious, where he had last fallen.

With the help of several soldiers Cárdenas removed the wounded man to a place of safety. Examination showed that the young general was badly hurt. He had suffered three wounds on his face, one in his leg — all made by arrows — and bruises over his entire body.

Although he remained unconscious for a long time, the loyal services of his faithful allies finally brought him to his senses. Although broken with pain and in doubt as to the fate of his army, he rejoiced to be told that the pueblo was taken. Best of all, when the Spaniards entered through the gate, they had found ample provisions within, especially quantities of maize. Already the nearly famished band had satisfied their stomachs and were now awaiting orders from their chief.

The general was happy to find the morale of the army at a high pitch. None of his wounded captains or men had any complaint to make as to their condition, but all were cheerful and contented, as became the soldiers of his Majesty's army. Coronado now learned that, in addition to the leaders injured in the attack, two or three soldiers were hurt in an encounter with Indians on the plain, and three horses killed, one belonging to García López de Cárdenas, another to Villegas, and the third to Don Alonso Manrique; also, that seven or eight horses were wounded.

The general was assured that in a short time both men and horses would be well.

Questioning his aids, he learned that in addition to maize the Indians of Cíbola generally had on hand a sufficient supply of beans and game. When asked about this, the Indians said that they did not eat game. The Spaniards did not believe the statement, because many skins of deer, hares and rabbits were strewn about the pueblo.

"These are the best tortillas I have ever tasted!" Coronado exclaimed, as he sampled for the first time the round, flattened cakes, fashioned from maize, and baked by the natives on heated stones.

"Yes, General," grinned Cárdenas. "These people have an ideal arrangement for grinding the maize. I am told that one of their women will grind as much in a given time as four Mexicans could. And their salt is formed of very good crystals — it is carried to the pueblo from a lake, a day's journey from here."

There were some fowl in the pueblo, but not many. The Indians told the general and his men that they did not make use of them as food, but kept them solely for their feathers. The Spaniards did not believe this statement.

"We have reconnoitered a little, General," said Cárdenas. "We have seen no fruits or fruit trees in Cíbola, and there are few firewood trees. The Indians carry what they need from a small clump of junipers, about four leagues distant from this place. About a quarter of a league distant there is very good grass; it could be used for pasturage for the horses, and for mowing and making hay. We need hay, for our mounts are greatly enfeebled at the present time.

"There are about two hundred houses in this pueblo — all are inside the walls. From a casual examination, we think there might be as many as five hundred in the section not surrounded by walls."

"What about the houses?" Coronado inquired.

Cárdenas smiled, a wry smile.

"Your Excellency has had a view of those," he replied. "But not from the roof tops!"

Still weak, Coronado nodded in assent.

Cárdenas continued:

"They are not decorated with turquoises to any extent, as we were led to believe, nor are they constructed of the best material, such as lime and bricks. Yet they are very good houses. Some are three, some four and some five stories high, and all have good rooms and corridors. There are also some very good rooms underneath the main section. These underground rooms, my men tell me, are well paved; evidently they are for winter use. They look like huge *estufas* [Spanish stoves]. However, they are used only for *kivas* or ceremonial chambers. As you have also observed, Excellency, the houses have ladders used for ascending to the higher stories, and these ladders may be carried from place to place. Your experience has acquainted you with the fact that these ladders are constructed of two pieces of wood, with rungs, like ours." Both men smiled, but somewhat wanly. The disappointment over what was found at Cíbola, so different from the cities of their expectations, still rankled.

"It does not seem that these Indians could have built the present houses," Cárdenas continued. "They seem to be fairly intelligent, as Your Excellency has doubtless observed, but not sufficiently skilled so as to have planned and executed this work."

When, by his order, a little group of the natives was brought to him, Coronado questioned them about their country.

They replied that it was very extensive, and that many animals were to be found there. These included bears, tigers, porcupines, and some sheep as big as the Spaniards' horses; these sheep, they said, had very large horns and very small tails.

They showed the general some of the horns — their size amazed him. They also showed him some heads of wild goats, the paws of bears and the skins of wild boars.

For game, they stated, there were deer, leopards and many large roebucks — all these were to be found some eight days' journey in the direction of the North Sea.

"I see you have some very well-dressed skins," Coronado observed. Through the interpreters the Indians told him that these skins were obtained from cattle which they killed and stripped in the place where they fell. The skins were then prepared and painted by the natives.

Coronado was well pleased when, three days after the taking of Cíbola, some of the Indians of the pueblo came to him to make peace. With them they brought some turquoises and poor blankets, the latter worked in colored patterns and, at a little distance, appearing as if painted.

The general welcomed them in the name of His Majesty the King. He spoke to them very kindly and made them understand the purpose of his coming to that country. He came, he said, in the name of His Majesty, and by the command of His Lordship, Don Antonio de Mendoza, to tell them that they, and all others in the province, should become Christians and should accept the true God as their King and the Emperor as their earthly Master.

The Indian messengers did not seem particularly well pleased by this announcement. However, they made no statement concerning their ideas on the subject, but returned to their houses in silence.

Coronado waited, hoping to learn that they had good news for him. But, on the very next day, he found that they had suddenly packed up their belongings and, taking their women and children with them, fled to the hills. Only a few remained behind in the pueblo.

The general and his men fully understood that they could obtain little treasure in the place. The Seven Cities of such alluring fame were actually only seven small villages, all having the same type of houses. Together they were called Cíbola. No one of them was impressive.

Coronado named the pueblo where he took up temporary residence Granada, because it bore a similarity to the Spanish Granada, the native place of Viceroy Mendoza.

As far as the general could ascertain, these Indians worshiped water because, they said, it caused the maize to grow and so maintained their life. The only other reason they did it, so far as they knew, was because their ancestors did it.

The memory of Estevan was often with Coronado during his sojourn in the pueblo. He was certain that the Moor was dead because a number of his articles which he had worn were found by the soldiers at Cíbola.

In answer to the general's persistent questioning, the Indians stated that they had killed the Moor "because he was a bad man, and not like the Christians, who never kill women." Estevan killed their women and assaulted them, and they loved their women better than themselves. Therefore, his death was accomplished.

They said, however, that they did not kill him in the manner previously reported. Nor did they hurt the boy from the province of Petatlán who was with him, but only took him into custody and held him, safe.

"Bring him to me!" the general ordered.

They were unwilling to do that. They offered various excuses for refusal during two or three days, when they conversed with Coronado. Sometimes they said that the boy was dead; again, that the Indians of Acucu had taken him away.

The young leader of the Spanish forces believed they were lying, and deemed it time that the boy was produced.

"If you do not bring him to me, I shall be very angry," he threatened.

The lad was speedily produced, for the people of Cíbola had no desire to experience any further trouble with their white conquerors. He was an interpreter, and, although not able to speak much, he understood very well what was said to him.

While the gold and silver about which the Spaniards had dreamed did not materialize, yet it was said that a certain amount of both metals had been found in the neighborhood of the Seven Cities, but no one knew where, or by whom. Coronado believed that, as on other occasions, his informants were withholding the truth or distorting it. In consequence, he ceased to expect the truth in anything they said. He was aware that they believed he soon would depart from their territory. He himself had stated this, but it was his hope that, before leaving, he could still wrest the facts from them.

On the nineteenth day of July Coronado journeyed four leagues from Cíbola on a reconnoitering tour. In particular he wished to inspect a rock where he was told some Indians of the province were holding out against the Spaniards. This rock was Towaylane, or Corn Mountain, the refuge of all the Indians of that country in time of danger.

Don Francisco ascertained to his entire satisfaction that

his men had followed his orders with respect to the treatment to be accorded the Indians of Cíbola. None of the native men or women had suffered wrong at the hands of his soldiers; the latter had not killed or inflicted cruelties upon any of them.

The young general was well pleased to learn this. And now he heard something that caused his heart to swell with happiness and gratitude. Questioning his faithful friend, López Cárdenas, about what had occurred after he himself was struck down from the rooftop the second time during the battle of Hawikuh, he learned how López had protected him in time of great danger by throwing himself over his prostrate leader.

"Good cavalier!" murmured the general, pressing the hand of the man who had proved his worth on many occasions, but never more significantly than in this deed of lofty heroism.

Naturally, Cárdenas was disappointed, as was his general, that the country on which they had set their hopes, was so poor and primitive.

"The land is sterile, General," he said. "We had hoped and believed otherwise. Now we know."

Coronado answered that this was true — they were deceived in regard to Cíbola. He thought it would be well to conduct further explorations in order to see if a better country could be found, "where God, our Lord, and His Majesty may be served and we ourselves benefited."

Don López García de Cárdenas was thinking, as he scrutinized the haggard face of his friend, that the lady Beatriz would hardly recognize her beloved, could she see him so worn and spent and covered with dark bruises and wounds. Surely, he thought, the prayers of her whose piety and gentleness had won for her the title "Saint" had saved the life of her husband in the grave peril to which he was exposed.

ON AUGUST 3, 1540, General Coronado wrote to his superior, Viceroy Mendoza, from Cíbola. In no happy frame of mind he composed the lines telling of the adventures of the army since the setting out from Culiacán on the twenty-second day of the preceding April. Wishing to acquaint Mendoza with the exact state of affairs at the very outset, he confessed openly:

"Judging by the outcome, I feel sure I was fortunate that I did not employ the whole of the army in this undertaking, because the hardships have been so very great and the lack of food such that I do not believe this enterprise could have been completed before the end of this year, and even if it could be accomplished, it would be with a great loss of life."

Don Francisco did not hesitate to reveal the festering wound in his heart caused by the report of the unhappy Fray Marcos de Niza. After recounting the hazards of the journey as far as the reconnaisance of Melchior Díaz, who went into rough mountainous country to see what could be found there, Coronado stated:

"From the people there, he [Díaz] learned that nothing could be found farther on except the continuation of the very rough mountains, entirely uninhabited by people. And, because this was wasted effort, I hasten to send your Lordship an account of it. The whole company felt displeased about this, that what had been so highly praised and about which the father had told so much, should turn out to be so very different; and they began to believe that all the rest would be the same."

The story of the continuation of the march, with swiftly succeeding disappointments shaking their confidence all the way, brought Fray Marcos de Niza again into the account of the general.

The men, he stated, were determined to proceed, after being encouraged by their leader. They resolved that nothing should deter them from going on to Cíbola and the other provinces of which they had heard. . . .

"With this resolution and purpose, we all marched cheerfully along a very bad trail, where it was impossible to travel without making a new road or clearing the one that was there. This troubled the soldiers not a little, seeing that everything which the friar had reported turned out to be quite the opposite; because, among other things which the father had told and affirmed, was that the road would be level and good, and that there was only one small hill, half a league long."

The general described for Mendoza the march to Corazones and the arrival at Chichilticalli, with its one miserable red-roofed ruin. He pointed out that again the statements of the friar were not borne out in fact in the findings of the disappointed men. They discovered that the sea turned toward the west for ten or twelve leagues directly opposite Corazones, "where I learned that the ships of your Lordship which had gone in search of the port of Chichilticalli, which the father said was at thirty-five degrees, had been seen."

The subsequent moves of the army were mentioned in detail by the general. No further mention of Fray Marcos de Niza was made, but Coronado disclosed the present needs of his men as follows:

"We are in great need of pasture, and you should know, also, that among all those who are here there is not one pound of raisins, nor sugar, nor oil, nor wine, except barely half a quart [of the latter] which is saved to say Mass, since everything has been consumed and part was lost on the way. . . .

"I would like to send you with this dispatch many samples of the things which they have in this country, but the trip is so long and rough that it is difficult for me to do so. However, I am sending you twelve small blankets such as the people of this country ordinarily wear, and a garment which seems to me to be very well made."

The general stated that this garment represented the first attempt at needlework on the part of the Indians that he had seen; that he also sent some painted cloths, turquoises and earrings made of the same, and wooden combs inlaid with the stones. . . .

"I also send two rolls, such as the women usually wear on their heads when they bring water from the spring, the same way they do in Spain. One of these Indian women, with one of these rolls on her head, will carry a jar of water up a ladder without touching it with her hands. Lastly, I send you samples of the weapons with which the natives of this country fight, a shield, a mallet [a short war club], and a bow with some arrows among which are two with bone points, the like of which have never been seen, according to what these conquerors say."

Referring to his sojourn in the pueblo of Hawikuh, which he had christened Granada, Don Francisco could give no definite information to Mendoza as to the length of time he expected to remain there before moving on to new fields of endeavor. The Indians of the place continued to be very evasive in their answers to his questions, refusing to give him any lead that might possibly result in the discovery of gold and silver. The samples of these metals found in the pueblo, as the general wrote the viceroy, were "said by those who knew metals to be not bad." However, he was forced to admit that he could ascertain nothing further on the subject.

By this time the young don had grown weary of his enforced inactivity and of the monotony of his surroundings. At Cíbola there was little excitement to divert the mind of a Spanish soldier. Each succeeding day he saw the same few figures moving solemnly about the pueblo. The Indian men wore no clothing except a piece of cloth, having fringes and a tassel at each corner, about the loins, with sometimes a cloak made of feathers or rabbit skins, or, occasionally cotton blankets draped about them. Their costume was certainly far less attractive than the elaborate dress of the "Christians" of New Spain.

These natives, exceedingly jealous of the honor of their women, had taken all of them from the pueblo in the flight after the storming of the walls, so that none of the army had been able to see any of them. However, the natives who remained behind described the women to the white men. They wore blankets tightly wrapped about their bodies and fastened over the left shoulder; the right arm was drawn over this garment. They gathered their hair over their ears in two great wheels resembling the puffs of a coif.

Don Francisco was well satisfied that the women were not there. Estevan the Moor had brought enough trouble on the Spaniards by his treatment of the Indian women who had followed him along his route north. Had the general no other reason to desire peace and quiet in the pueblo, the bumps and cuts on his head and body were more than sufficient to remind him of it.

When he was strong enough to walk about the place,

Coronado examined everything with much curiosity and interest.

The Indians of Hawikuh were accustomed to plant their corn in holes; it did not grow to any great height but each single stalk bore from two to four ears. He was told that these ears contained approximately eight hundred grains each. Just now the stalks showed green and flourishing, for the harvest was near at hand.

There were numerous *estufas* in the pueblo. Deep down within their circular walls the councils of the natives were held. In one of these, assuredly, the fate of Estevan the Moor was decided.

"These Indians have no ruler, as we do in Spain," Cárdenas said to his chief as the two walked together through the place. "They are governed by the council of their oldest men. Their priests are called *papas* and they preach to the people. This is done at the rising of the sun, when the papas mount on high terraces to perform their office. The people are seated along the paths of the pueblo in front of their houses, and they listen to the preachers in silence. The Cíbola Indians are not barbarous — we have found no trace of human bones lying about anywhere within the walls. They cremate their dead, but many other tribes do this, as you know. Like other Indians, they burn with the bodies any implements the departed used for work during their lifetime."

As he finished his brief account, Cárdenas handed his young leader some piñon nuts, which both men munched like schoolboys.

But Coronado could no longer remain inactive. His quest for treasure had begun long ago. When he had gone to Culiacán to take up the reins of government, on the demise of Torre, successor to the infamous Nuño de Guzmán, he had first heard of a rich region to the north, called Topira. In a letter to Viceroy Mendoza at that time, as the recently appointed governor of Nueva Galicia, he had described this land in the most glowing terms. He stated that he was told it was densely populated, and that the natives there "wear gold and emeralds and other precious stones." The air was filled with such rumors.

With Mendoza's sanction, Coronado had at that time set out from Culiacán with a party of three hundred and fifty men to explore this reputedly rich region. But he did not find it, and returned with no report save one of complete failure.

Then came property troubles, when rights concerning some of his holdings were questioned by Francisco Morales, sent to fill the post of relator to the audiencia in Mexico City. It was to be expected that even now Don Francisco would like to know how events were going in relation to these properties, as well as in regard to other matters in which he was interested. In Mexico, for instance, the young don enjoyed the reputation of being a deeply religious and charitable man — he was an organizer and charter member of the Brotherhood of the Blessed Sacrament for Charity, an association of laymen founded in Mexico City in 1538 to help needy persons, especially to educate orphan girls.

But Coronado had never allowed his charitable disposition to interfere with his determination to punish severely any and all who opposed his designs for the good of the Church and that of Spain, and he had shown himself no less eager to report the great need of friars to teach the ignorant and superstitious brown men the truths of the Christian religion and the desirability of their obedience to the crown.

He thought now of the dishonored Fray Marcos de Niza whom he, as did every other Spaniard in the army, held responsible for the frustration of well-laid plans of conquest. Formerly Coronado had deemed otherwise of the gentle spiritual son of Saint Francis. The kindly treatment accorded by Fray Marcos to all the natives he met on the first northward journey had served to prepare the way for a generous reception for the general and his men. Hawikuh alone was the exception — but Hawikuh was now subjugated and it remained for the army only to pass beyond it and find whether there was something much more worth while to engage their attention.

In his own communication by letter with Mendoza, written on March 8 of the previous year, at the very time the friar was starting on his journey, Don Francisco had said of him and his relations with the Indians of Petatlán and other places, who were given him as his escort:

"They carried the Padre on the palms of their hands, pleasing him in everything they could."

Now that the grumblings and lightning flashes of pain, engendered by his many wounds and bruises, had somewhat died away, and his soldier's body began to thrill anew with the zest for high adventure, perhaps Don Francisco Vásquez de Coronado did not feel so highly indignant with the little friar . . . he might even feel a little sorry for Fray Marcos de Niza.

XXIII

HIS HEART oppressed by sorrow and his spirit crushed by the sinister turn of events which had robbed him of joy and reputation alike, Fray Marcos de Niza set out from Hawikuh Pueblo early in August for the return to Mexico. Coronado remained within the walls, where he was to sojourn until November before proceeding on the quest for new and better fields of endeavor.

Accompanying the dejected friar were two Spanish captains, Melchior Díaz and Juan Gallego, who were going to Corazones, the Valley of the Hearts, to deliver a message from their general to the section of the army that had remained behind. Fray Marcos was only too glad to escape from the presence of Don Francisco and his soldiers.

Nature herself seemed more friendly than man to the friar in this difficult hour. From the occasional piñon shrubs growing along the way the three companions gathered a little supply of the juicy nuts to serve as refreshment later on, when vegetation should have disappeared from their path. Growing to a height of about twice the measure of a man, great gray smudges against the cliffs, the piñon plants reminded the son of Saint Francis that God's loving providence was still over all. Not man, but God cared for the sturdy piñons, casting the seeds, watering and tending them, and enabling them to become a useful gift from heaven to man. A slow but perfect work was accomplished in them, for a period of two full years was required from the blossoming stage of the plant to the resinous purple cone.

At Corazones the soldiers of the rear guard were happy to greet their captain, Díaz, and to learn that they were now free to travel to rejoin their comrades in the north. Fray Marcos de Niza they treated with scant courtesy after they had heard the report on the Seven Cities as given by Díaz.

Melchior Díaz remained in command of Corazones. He had received orders from his general to institute a search for Alarcón's ships, sent out previously to scout along the coast in the hope of aiding the land forces. Díaz ordered eighty soldiers to stay behind in the Valley of the Hearts in order to maintain a supply center for the rest of the army; for the ships, should they find them, and for the "homeland" of Nueva España.

Fray Marcos took up his journey with Captain Juan Gallego. The latter proved to be a not unpleasant companion along the way. However, Fray Marcos knew that under the circumstances the captain had to make the best of something that might not be to his liking. When a man travels through lonely country with but one other human being, he is forced to make the best of the company.

One of the settlers of the post of Purificación, in 1536, Captain Gallego's effects were listed on the muster roll of the expedition: "A coat of mail and breeches, buckskin coat, crossbow and other Castilian and native weapons, and seven horses."

Close to his heart the captain carried a very important paper. It was the report, drawn up by Coronado and addressed to the most noble viceroy. Although Gallego did not know its contents, he suspected that his traveling companion of the Order of Saint Francis came in for his share of the blame in the matter of the crushing disappointment suffered at Hawikuh.

Both men would have given much to know what the general had written, for the names of both occurred frequently in the report.

Concerning the role played by the friar in the expedition, Coronado had written:

"Thirty leagues before reaching the place, I sent Melchior Díaz ahead with fifteen horsemen, ordering him to make one day's journey out of two, so that he could examine everything there before I arrived. He traveled through some very rough country for four days and did not find anything to live on, nor people, nor information about anything; all he found was two or three poor villages, with twenty or thirty huts each. From the people he learned that nothing could be found farther on except the continuation of the very rough mountains, entirely uninhabited by people. And, because this was wasted effort, I hesitated to send your Lordship an account of it. The whole company felt displeased at this, that what had been so highly praised and about which the father had told so much, should turn out to be so very different; and they began to believe that all the rest would be of the same sort. . . ."

In another part of his letter, Coronado wrote:

"We all marched cheerfully along a very bad trail, where it was impossible to travel without making a new road or clearing the one that was there. This troubled the soldiers not a little, seeing that everything which the friar had reported turned out to be quite the opposite, because, among other things the father had told and affirmed, was the report that the road would be level and good, and that there was only one small hill, half a league long. And the truth is that there are mountains where, however well the path might be repaired, they could not be crossed without there being a great danger of the horses rolling down. And it was so bad that a large number of animals which your Lordship sent as provisions for the army were lost along this part of the way, on account of the roughness of the rocks."

Other unfavorable details succeeded, until there came further mention of Fray Marcos de Niza. Concerning Corazones, for instance, the general wrote: "The sea turns toward the west for ten or twelve leagues directly opposite Corazones, where I learned that the ships of your Lordship which had gone in search of the port of Chichilticalli, which the father said was at thirty-five degrees, had been seen. . . ."

"It now remains to tell about the Seven Cities, the kingdom and province, of which the father . . . gave your Lordship an account. Not to be too verbose, I can assure you that he has not told the truth in a single thing that he said, but everything is the opposite of what he related, except the name of the cities and the large stone houses. . . ."

"The kingdom of Tontonteac, which the father . . . praised so highly, saying it was something marvelous and of much richness, and that cloth was made there, is, according to the Indians, a hot lake, on the edge of which there are five or six houses."

Beneath his "buckskin coat," the blithe Captain Gallego carried the precious document which so bluntly conveyed the idea of the friar's supposed unreliability. With the intuitivism of the scholar and explorer, as well as man of God, Fray Marcos knew that this was so. He accepted the trial in the spirit of his holy Rule, with docility and resignation, although his heart was sorely burdened with the weight of it.

The Franciscan pioneer had other troubled thoughts to

keep him company. There was the brackish remembrance of the omnipresent Cortés, who had accused him of willful misrepresentations at various times in his career. Others would not be slow to adopt Cortés' ideas on this subject — barbers, for instance! Fray Marcos believed that Viceroy Mendoza would be somewhat more generous in his estimate of him than was Coronado. He was unaware of the testimonial given by Mendoza on this point. For, when the viceroy forwarded a copy of the friar's report to His Majesty the Emperor, referring to him and Brother Onorato, Mendoza had written:

"These friars lived for some time in the neighboring countries; they were used to hard labor, experienced in the ways of the Indians, conscientious and of good habits." The fact that Mendoza had sent Melchior Díaz to explore, in order to confirm, if possible, what the friar had said about the northern provinces, did not necessarily imply that Mendoza disbelieved in Fray Marcos' veracity — doubtless he understood something of the difficulties involved in getting at facts, such as the unreliability of the Indians in their statements, and similar considerations.

Just two months previous to this time, Cortés, appearing before the Spanish Court, in his formal petition against Mendoza had told of his purported meeting with Fray Marcos. A thorn in the side of Mendoza, he had become equally so to the friar. The latter had given his oath in Mexico City, on September 22, 1539, that he had made the journey to Cíbola as stated. On the second day of that month he had appeared to testify before Mendoza in relation to the Cortés statement, as follows:

Fray Marcos testified that he had received no information whatever from Hernando Cortés about the new countries he had explored — Cortés and Mendoza were at the time parties to a dispute as to whether the Marques' contract with the king gave him special rights of exploration in the north. This contention was strongly opposed by the viceroy.

Fray Marcos also stated that he had made the journey to Cíbola by the viceroy's orders, making use of the Indian guides provided by Mendoza to lead the way. The friar astutely remarked, at the time, that if Cortés had actually received any information about the "new countries," he would hardly have sent two of his ships to the aid of Pizarro in Peru — this he had done in 1535.

Five witnesses were present at the deposition of the friar; they were Francisco de Ceinos, Francisco Vásquez de Coronado, Fray Martin de Ojacastro and two notaries.

Fray Marcos di Niza knew of but one man in all the Indies, outside of the brethren of his Order, on whom he could count to sustain him in his trial. That man was the saintly Bishop Juan de Zumárraga, who had introduced him to Mendoza with the recommendation that he was the person pre-eminently well fitted to execute the important commission the viceroy had in mind.

Clearly, the path of one who would sacrifice himself in the fulfillment of mighty projects for the Divine Majesty and for an earthly sovereign was beset with many hardships and sufferings of mind, as well as body. The pains in his joints, added to those he endured mentally, assured Fray Marcos de Niza that this was so.

The parting of the friar and Gallego from Melchior Díaz, who was to remain at Corazones, consumed little time. Fray Marcos and Juan, going forward at a rapid pace in their desire to reach Mexico as soon as possible, gave no further thought to the fortunes of their former companion on the way. They little realized that they were never to see the gallant captain again in this world.

After his two friends had left the Valley of the Hearts, Díaz at once swung into action to carry out the orders of his chief, Coronado.

Selecting twenty-five men to accompany him, he made the trip to the Gulf of California. Thence the party traveled in a northerly direction until they came to the junction of two rivers, the Gila and the Colorado. Seeing the Indians of the place carrying firebrands with which they warmed themselves, exchanging them from one hand to another for the purpose, the Spanish soldiers christened the river the Tizon, or Firebrand River.

The Indians told the strangers that they had seen other white men and ships in that vicinity. Looking about him, Diaz soon discovered an inscription cut into a tree. It read: "There are letters at the foot of this tree."

The captain at once dug into the soil at the foot of the tree. In a few minutes he came upon the letters. In them Alarcón, captain of Coronado's ships, said that he had waited in vain for a sight of the general and his men, but had been disappointed upon failing to sight them. The ships began to rot in the strong sun and Alarcón found it necessary to move onward.

Melchior Díaz and his party crossed the river on rafts. When they again found themselves on land they experienced some opposition from the Yuma Indians, who did not want them to pass through their lands. Overcoming this opposition, they started down the west side of the Colorado River into Lower California. Soon the passage became blocked by volcanic lava beds, and they were obliged to turn back.

Heading for Corazones and the supply station, Díaz met with a tragic accident which resulted in a painful death for the brave captain.

Observing that a greyhound belonging to a Spanish soldier was carrying off one of the sheep belonging to the expedition, he started in pursuit of the marauder. His horse was galloping at full speed when he hurled his lance in the direction of the dog.

Díaz missed aim and the weapon lodged in the earth at the horse's feet. It was too late to guide the beast away from it. Man and horse fell, and the lance pierced Díaz' abdomen.

Stunned by the happening, his men rallied to the aid of their leader. For a number of days they carried him, as gently as possible, in the hope of reaching Corazones and saving his life. However, their hopes were not fulfilled, and Díaz expired shortly before they reached the army station. This was on January 18, 1541, long after Fray Marcos de Niza was re-established in Mexico and carrying on his former missionary work of caring for sick souls and bodies.

Many significant tasks had been entrusted by his general to Captain Díaz. Although, as the historian of the expedition, Pedro de Castañada, wrote at a later date, not a "gentleman" by birth, Díaz merited the post he held. As Mayor of Culiacán he had freed the natives whom Diego de Alcarez had taken unlawfully to use as his slaves. This he did at the request of Cabeza de Vaca, whom he received at that place.

The other distinguished services Díaz had rendered likewise revealed him to be a man of ability and honor. Many times his life was in grave danger, and many times he had escaped unharmed from difficult and perilous situations.

In the strange and unpredictable anomaly of human affairs a dishonest dog had brought to his death the man who had never failed in the performance of his duty or in loyalty to his chief.

XXIV

BECAUSE, as Coronado had stated in his letter to Mendoza, the wine supply had failed, Fray Marcos, traveling through the sterile region directly north of San Miguel de Culiacán on his way to the capital, was deprived of the great source of strength and consolation of the priest — the privilege of saying Mass.

His sole possession apart from the poor garments he wore was a bundle containing the sacred vestments. And when, at night, he stretched himself out on the hard earth to sleep fitfully, the cold light of dawn breaking in the east brought anew the realization of his shattered hopes and the stigma that now attached to his once honored name.

His companion, Captain Juan Gallego, slept soundly after the long day's march, his heart light under his cherished "buckskin coat." If he felt any sympathy for the plight of the lonely little friar he did not allude to it, for a Spanish soldier wore his heart inside, not outside his armor.

Fray Marcos found some comfort in prayer and meditation, yet even these failed to wholly relieve the distress which agitated his being. The realization that those who were now his adversaries, and who mistrusted and scorned him, were formerly his friends, gave added pain to his heart. His sensitive Savoyard imagination only served to animate images he could wish to put from him, together with unhappy thoughts and fears for the future. Happily, he could still remember that his Saviour had suffered in like manner, only His sufferings were aggravated beyond comparison with the sharpest woes of any of His creatures.

Once before, in dire extremity, Fray Marcos de Niza had yearned for one to whom he could turn for counsel and inspiration. Inscribed in the Relación of his high adventure of the previous year was a confidence — touching in its sincerity and humility — the avowal of his inability to cope with a trying, even desperate situation:

"God is my witness of how much I wished to have someone with whom to take counsel and advice, for I must confess that I did not know what to do." Such were his sentiments when, after the news of Estevan's death was returned, the Indians muttered dark threats against his life. . . . Now Fray Marcos de Niza, sitting in the cactus-strewn solitude, remembered that incident and prayed that help would come to him.

As always, after the first harsh sting of suffering had somewhat abated, a blessed light shone in upon his soul. He pictured to himself the blithe-hearted Saint of Assisi, dancing through the lonely wilderness of sand and spine. Francis would have loved the most unfriendly habitat of this barren desert. He would be able to forget any sorrows of his own as he searched the faces of the Indians, and his manly heart would be moved to tears at the thought of the spiritual desolation of a forgotten and aloof people.

Inscrutable in their thoughts, solitary in their habits, inured for longer than any white man could know to physical and mental endurance, and loving their own primitive uncultivated ways, the Indians, nevertheless, while at first dour and uncompromising toward the white

man, became friendly and companionable when once
they understood and believed in the honesty of his purpose. These first citizens of the New World awaited the
coming of the messengers of Jesus Christ, His missionaries. So Viceroy Mendoza and General Coronado had
assured His Majesty the King, and the monarch was only
too desirous of winning them to Christianity, as well as
ensuring their submission to the Crown.

Fray Marcos had experienced intimate associations
with the brown men of the New World from the time of
his first visit to Peru with the Spaniard, Alvarado, in
January of 1534. The friars of that place had brought
about his election as *custodio,* and he had enjoyed the
happiness of a close friendship with Bishop Juan de
Zumárraga. Another great bishop, a Dominican, Las
Casas, would shortly draw up an important paper, in-
corporating in it the testimony of Fray Marcos de Niza
regarding the cruel treatment accorded the Indians by
the Spaniards in Peru.

Although most zealous for the conversion of these ignorant and idol-worshiping peoples, the "Christians"
were often exceedingly harsh and unjust in their methods
of attaining their ends with them. Hernando Cortés and
his followers had demonstrated this on a gigantic scale in
Mexico; Francisco Pizarro had done the same in Peru.
Intemperate in their approach to the things the natives
held sacred, the Spaniards first attempted to win them
by force, thinking that afterwards the Indians would willingly embrace the faith of their new masters.

One especially touching incident within the friar's
memory well illustrated the tenacity with which the
brown men clung to the religion and customs of their
ancestors. It now recurred to his mind to strengthen the
very points he had made famous in his defense of their
rights and privileges.

This incident took place in connection with the execution of the young and beloved Inca Prince, Atahualpa, at Caxamalca, Peru, when Fray Marcos stood in the group surrounding the unfortunate ruler and witnessed proceedings as heartless and inhuman as they were unjust and unchristian.

Certain rumors, later proved to be without solid foundation, were bruited about, to the effect that Atahualpa had plotted an uprising among the natives, which was calculated to defeat the Spanish arms. Hernando Pizarro, the conqueror of Peru, approached the Inca Prince and accused him of this. Atahualpa pleaded his innocence in the most heart-rending way. He had believed the Spanish chief to be his friend; he had trusted him and relied on his promises of friendship. Now, it seemed, this reliance was misplaced, and the fate of the Inca rested in the hands of this man of indomitable will and inflexible purpose.

An examination produced nothing in favor of Atahualpa's innocence nor did it indicate his guilt. Yet sentence of execution was passed, and Spanish trumpets announced the fact as they sounded in the great plaza of Caxamalca two hours after the sun had set.

Thus summoned to the presence of their leader, the Spaniards saw the deposed Indian ruler brought forward, chained hand and foot, his face a mask of mingled pain, surprise and fear. At his side a gray-robed Franciscan friar walked, holding up a crucifix and striving to offer consolation to the doomed man. This friar, Father Valverde, had tried for a long time to win Atahualpa to the Christian faith, but so far to no avail.

Fray Marcos de Niza's heart had swelled with righteous indignation at the sight of the Inca being chained to a stake, at the foot of which a pile of faggots were in readiness for the application of the torch which should set them ablaze. Father Valverde held the crucifix closer to the Inca's face, begging him to kiss it.

Finally, the friar promised that if the Inca would renounce pagan beliefs and embrace the Christian religion his sentence would be commuted to garroting.

Atahualpa asked if this was really so. On being told that it was, he renounced his ancient beliefs and was immediately baptized by the friar. He was given the name, Juan, because the day marked the Feast of Saint John the Baptist.

Fray Marcos had witnessed many instances of the Indians' deep-rooted love for their own, particularly for their children. But never had he encountered a more touching proof of this love than now. For the betrayed prince besought as a last favor of Pizarro that the conquistador would have pity on his young children and exercise a paternal care over them.

Soon the penalty of trusting too much was paid in full. The friars prayed all night over the remains of the dead prince, left lying in the plaza as an example to those who would dare contravene the white man's will.

Still another striking proof of the Indians' fidelity to their own was manifested on the following morning, when Fray Marcos, with other friars, attended the obsequies of the slain Inca. Father Valverde was in the midst of the rites when, suddenly, he was interrupted by a burst of wailing and a thumping on the outer door of the church. Then the door was thrown open and a group of Indian women rushed up the aisle. They ran to the body of the deceased, some of them throwing themselves on his coffin, others surrounding it, all striving to get as close as possible to him whom they had deeply loved in life. These were the wives and sisters of Atahualpa.

Defiantly, they insisted that the Mass was not the proper service for their dead, and protested that they were determined to take their own lives and so accompany their loved one to the land of spirits, rather than live without him on earth.

The efforts of the friars to pacify the women were all in vain. In vain did the men of God try to explain to them that the Christians held in abomination such a sacrifice of human life as that which they proposed to offer. The women were finally induced to leave the church, but the Spaniards later learned that a number of them had executed their threat and had died by their own hand, in the fond hope of journeying with the dead Atahualpa to the glorious mansions of the Sun.

In the long eventful journey to Cíbola Fray Marcos everywhere had found the Indians trying to establish communication between themselves and the great spirit, whom they believed resided in physical things, such as water and fire. He remembered how delighted they were when he prayed over their sick and laid his anointed hand upon them. "Man From Heaven," they called him, as they vaguely tried to discover some link between one who did them so much good and the spirit whom they adored.

Fray Marcos de Niza did not know how much missionary work, if any, awaited him in Mexico, or how much he would be able to accomplish in the time that might lie ahead. His body, stiff and sore from prolonged traveling through rough country; weakened by exposure to the unkind elements, by hunger and want of every kind, and now exposed to further ravages by reason of the heavy mental depression never long absent from him, plainly showed the effects of the terrible strain imposed upon it. Estevan's murder was the first bitter blow to his plans — he had never fully recovered from the shock of it. This was succeeded by fears for his own life; by ever increasing difficulties with the Indians, who blamed him for the death of their relatives who accompanied Estevan, and, finally, by the sad stern disillusionment of finding, before the walls of Hawikuh, all his holy desires and hopes crushed and scattered and himself become the object of the Spaniards' contempt and wrath.

Fray Marcos, journeying homeward over the rough and desert ways, was not without courage. There was yet a task he could do. He could fulfill the role of missionary in whatever manner his frail strength might allow, until such time as God might strengthen him, or call him to Himself.

As he broke his fast with a meager portion of food carried from Hawikuh, there came to his pale lips the prayer the friars recited far back in his beloved Nice, when, elevating their hands over the bread and cakes set apart for the poor, they besought:

"Lord Jesus Christ, Bread of Angels, Bread of the Living and of eternal life, bless and make worthy this bread as Thou didst bless the bread in the desert; that all who partake of it worthily, may obtain the desired health of body and soul alike. Amen."

Over the desert the sun rose in silent glory, bringing warmth and color to the waking earth.

As Fray Marcos de Niza watched its rays slowly lengthening over the tops of the cactus and the uneven stretches of tawny sand, they appeared like the glorified Fingers of a wounded Hand, beckoning to fairer fields of conquest. . . .

XXV

IN JALAPA, the capital city of Vera Cruz, Mexico, Fray Marcos de Niza found refuge at the close of his hazardous and trying mission.

The harsh experience of the past years had told on his health. He was no longer able to travel abroad or to perform any task that required great physical endurance. A slow creeping paralysis appeared to be settling over his limbs, rendering locomotion difficult. It was apparent that in a short time hands and feet would be wholly crippled.

By degrees news of General Coronado and the Spanish army reached the friar in his isolated retreat. All had not gone well with the gallant Don Francisco since Fray Marcos left him behind at Hawikuh. The expedition had ventured into other parts, but the outcome was much like that of Cíbola. It had failed to find material treasure and had suffered many embarrassments and defeats in its hardy reconnoitering.

From Hawikuh, Fray Marcos learned, Coronado and his men had set out to explore the surrounding country. One of the Spanish captains, Pedro de Tovar, while traveling with Fray Juan de Padilla, a friar, and a band of twenty soldiers, had discovered the Hopi pueblos. At first the Hopi Indians gave battle for the right to live unmolested, but eventually they surrendered to the white men. Their territory, called by its inhabitants Tusayan, proved to be lacking in gold or other treasure, and Don Pedro returned in dejection to report his findings to his chief. He stated, however, that the Hopis had told him of the existence of a great river to westward.

Coronado commissioned Cárdenas, his faithful friend, to explore this river. Cárdenas set out on his mission, and came upon the Grand Canyon of the Colorado. Even this wonder of nature, yielded no gold, and again the general and his men suffered keen disappointment.

From a pueblo to the east, called Cicuye, Indians came to invite the general to pay them a visit. The bearer of this message of goodwill was a giant called Bigotes. Coronado sent Captain Alvarado and Fray Juan de Padilla, with twenty men and native guides, to explore the country of which Bigotes spoke. They did so, and discovered the sky pueblo of Acoma, where they made peace with its people.

Later, traveling eastward, they reached the verdant valley of the Rio Grande and the Tiguex Province. On the return to Cicuye they met an Indian, named by them The Turk, "because he looked like one." Under his guidance they explored to the east, and, after crossing the mountains, entered the Texas panhandle with its extensive plains. Here they caught their first glimpse of Cabeza de Vaca's "cows," buffaloes, and were amazed by the gigantic creatures.

The Turk now told the Spaniards of a land called Quivira, where, he asserted, even the most common utensils were made of pure gold. Coronado rejoiced to receive this report. After making arrangements for winter quarters for his men in that place, he himself set out to explore a province called Tutahaco, near the site of the modern Isleta, New Mexico, and later joined Cárdenas at a pueblo called Alcanfor, where Alvarado and his men, with The Turk, awaited his coming.

Although not satisfied that The Turk was telling the truth in his tale of wonders, the general set out from Alcanfor, traveling with his entire army toward Quivira. On the way he met a tribe of Indians called Querechos. They were nomads, and gave the Spaniards some information about pueblos lying farther east. On its way the army met many obstacles, but the worst disappointment of all awaited them when Quivira [near the modern Wichita, Kansas] was finally reached. Only a village of disreputable straw shacks met their gaze. Again they tasted the bitterest dregs of despair and disillusionment. As a reward for his deception, The Turk was garrotted, after previously admitting that, according to a deep-laid plot, he had purposely misled the white men in order that they might be massacred on the desolate plains.

Later, scouting parties of soldiers visited the Queres settlements, with their pueblos of Santo Domingo, San Felipe, Santa Ana, Zía and Cochití, thence proceeding in a northerly direction to Taos. Other bands of the soldiers went westward and reached Guadaloupe Canyon, to be known as the Jemez Province. All these places were located in territory later to become New Mexico.

After many bewildering and blighting experiences, but with no realization of the fact that they had discovered a great portion of a new country which one day would constitute a treasure of untold worth, the general and his men set out for Mexico. An advance guard composed of disabled soldiers traveled under escort of Cárdenas, who himself had broken an arm. When this group reached Corazones, the Valley of the Hearts, they were shocked to find the town in ruins and to learn that all its inhabitants had been massacred.

Before leaving the north General Coronado himself suffered a disastrous injury. While racing his horse with that of one of his captains his saddle girth gave way and he was thrown directly in the path of his companion's racing steed. The hoofs of the beast struck Coronado in the head, rendering him unconscious. Throughout the second winter spent by the army in the north he remained critically ill, so that his recovery seemed doubtful. However, in the spring of 1542 he was able to set forth for home with the rest of the army. Only a group of Franciscan friars remained behind, to labor for the conversion of the native tribes, and to win martyrdom as a reward for their zeal.

Fray Marcos de Niza was to learn still more of the later fortunes of Don Francisco Vásquez de Coronado. The general had returned to his post as governor of Nueva Galicia, but his days were filled with troubles and disturbances. Tried on charges resulting from his conduct of the Cíbola expedition, he was acquitted of any fault on that score. But on the other hand he was judged guilty of maladministration during his tenure of office as governor, and was fined by being deprived of certain pueblos and of natives he had acquired as his property. His ally, Captain Cárdenas, was declared guilty of grave offenses in connection with the northern expedition and was imprisoned for a term of five years.

Don Francisco's health was never restored after his latest misfortunes. Moreover, his mind remained clouded as a result of the head injury suffered from the horse's hoofs, and he died in the autumn of 1554.

Viceroy Mendoza, while remaining a friend to Coronado, had lost confidence in his leadership and consequently failed to entrust him with any important commission after the close of the expedition. Mendoza left Mexico to become viceroy of Peru. But he died only a short time after taking office. His demise occurred in the city of Lima, in July of 1552, about two years before the passing of Don Francisco Vásquez de Coronado.

Fray Marcos de Niza was to outlive both the men who had played such an important role in his fortunes in the New World. In the hospital at Jalapa, where he ministered to the sick, he continued to labor zealously. His time was spent mainly in hearing confessions, preaching, consoling those who suffered, and preparing the dying for their journey out of this world.

Jalapa, where the Spaniards had taken up residence soon after the Conquest because of its convenient location and agreeable climate, was a veritable garden of delights. Girt about by imposing mountain ranges and with its ever blooming tierra caliente, a panorama of bewitching beauty, lying below, it reminded Fray Marcos of his cherished Nice and was a source of perennial contentment to his tired heart.

Towering far above the valley, the conelike peak of Orizaba, robed in glistening snows, seemed a monarch in ermine, standing erect and majestic in his stronghold. To this august summit, according to Aztec belief, Quetzalcoatl, God of the Air, was borne after his death, and there his body was consumed by a mighty sheet of flame. His subjects believed that one day their god would return to their midst.

In striking contrast to the cold purity of Orizaba, the pine-girt mountains of the Sierra Madre towered above the lower hills melting behind them into the distance. Of these, the Cofre de Perote, shaped, as its name indicated, like a great coffer, was the most impressive because its porphorytic composition caused it to shine brilliantly in the sun's rays. To the Indians it was Nauchampatepetl, "Square Mountain."

Fray Marcos was consoled when at the bedsides of the sick he came upon great masses of blossoms gathered from the valleys and gardens, or when their fragrance breathed upon him from the feet of Maria Purisima. It was she, the blessed Patroness of the Spanish people, who, when the sun refused to shine in Jalapa, brought it back by her prayers to her Son.

The worn little friar was always cold in body, even in the month of May, which in Jalapa was the warmest month of the year. Especially severe were the twinges in his bones and muscles when the clouds, laden with moisture from the gulf, rolled over the mountains and discharged their burden on the town. Then came days of continuous mist, a dull drizzle that blotted out all beauty and light. La Llovizna, the people called the mist, and prayed to Maria Purisima to take it away soon.

XXVI

BY ORDER of his provincial, Fray Marcos de Niza was removed from Jalapa to Xochimilco, town of the floating gardens, where many traces of the Conquest remained to tell of the triumphant issue of the Spanish arms over the old Aztec methods of warfare.

A little island, surrounded by waterways whose numerous drawbridges intersected the streets at many points, it had witnessed stirring episodes of history. Here Hernando Cortés had waged a stubborn battle with the natives, coming near to losing his life when, in the midst of the enemy, his horse's hoofs had sunk deep in the mire, and the redoubtable general was thrown into the mud. To an Indian ally Cortés owed his preservation, for without the timely intervention of this native he must have fallen into the hands of his adversaries.

The death of Bishop Juan de Zumárraga, in the early summer of 1548, had removed the one man upon whom Fray Marcos had long relied, and whose faithful friendship had never failed him. Soon after his return from the great adventure with Coronado's men, the friar had realized that he must have some help for his weakened body, as well as renewed courage for his sorely-tried heart and mind. A little medicine would provide the relief so greatly needed that he might continue to do even the light work assigned to him.

To the good bishop he had dictated a letter in which he made known this need:

"With all reverence and devotion," the letter read, "I kiss the feet and hands of Your Reverence, and with devotion I ask your paternal benediction. You will know that, on account of having left the hot country, my health has become very bad. On this account the father provincial orders me to Xochimilco. As I, an orphan, have no father or mother, friend or refuge, except your lordship, whom I have found more than a father in all my necessities, and all without meriting it, through the exceeding charity of your lordship, I supplicate your lordship to make me, for a few months, a little donation of wine, of which I am in great need, as my sickness is lack of blood and natural heat. I will receive it as the greatest charity; and if you can do this, write me for how many months and how much your lordship wishes to give, so I can send an Indian to get it at the proper time. Praying that the Lord God will guard and save your reverend person, from this, your house, Friday, the lowest servant and chaplain of your lordship. Fray Marcos de Niza."

Fray Marcos held in his possession as a precious souvenir the letter sent by the kindly bishop in reply to this appeal. It was, as the recipient had known it would be, most generous and consoling:

"To this I say, father of mine, servant of God, that during the years and months that I shall live, while your sickness and necessity last, every month an arroba of wine shall be given to you. And from the present I send it to you and order Martin de Aranguren to give you, for my account, of the best that there is, and the hospital overseer, Lucas, or his companion, will give it to the Indian who comes for it, if I should not be in this city. February 27, 1546." In a postscript, the bishop wrote: "If more should be necessary, it will be given with a good will."

Bishop Zumárraga had lived but a little more than two

years after the writing of this letter. His going left a void in many hearts, but in none greater than in the heart of Fray Marcos, whose burden the saintly prelate had rendered much lighter by reason of his charity.

Born at Durango, in the Basque Provinces, the bishop had entered the Franciscan Order in his youth. When the full import of the conquest of the Aztec kingdom by Cortés was felt in Spain, Juan de Zumárraga was recommended by Charles V as the ecclesiastic best fitted to become first bishop of Mexico. With the titles of Bishop-elect, and Protector of the Indians — not having as yet been consecrated — he had sailed from Spain for Mexico, reaching the latter country in December of 1528.

From the first, the Bishop-elect was subject to trial and embarrassment from the auditors, whose authority was shared by the cruel Nuño de Guzmán. In the absence of Cortés in Spain, these three men had carried on an administration of injustice and rapacity. The bishop found himself called on to fulfill to the limit his role of Protector of the natives, who were being persecuted and robbed of their little possessions by the Spanish rulers. Other trials pressed on Bishop Zumárraga, including calumnies uttered against him by his own countrymen, who resented his defense of the Indians. The appointment of Don Antonio de Mendoza as first viceroy of Nueva España put an end to many of these trials.

After years of devoted service to the Church and to Spain, the bishop could spend his declining years in organizing and promoting various good works of charity and education. He had introduced the printing press into the New World, founded schools and hospitals, and performed other works of the greatest utility. In particular, he had approved the devotion to the Virgin of Guadalupe, after examining into the statements of the Mexican peasant to whom she appeared. From that time she became the special patroness of the Mexican people, under her new title.

When, in 1546, at the request of the Emperor, Pope Paul III separated the See of Mexico from that of Seville and erected the archdiocese of Mexico, Bishop de Zumárraga was designated as its first archbishop. The bull of approval was sent on July 8, 1548, but Bishop de Zumárraga had died the previous month.

Fray Marcos de Niza could be forever thankful that in the hour of distress, when others deserted him, this great man had remained steadfast and loyal in his friendship.

Now it was the gentle friar's pleasure to watch the Indians of Xochimilco move silently over the current of the waters in their primitive rafts, or wait patiently beside the banks of the streams for a catch of the small fish, resembling trout, which abounded in the vicinity.

The famed floating gardens of the town were loveliest at the hours of sunrise and sunset, when the heavy masses of flowers, supported on mattresses of twigs, drifted along the canals, sprayed by opalescent tints from the meadows of the sky. The natives propelled these rafts with oars. Some of the floating gardens were decorated with tiny huts, about which many varieties of plants and blossoms were arranged to resemble a great flower-bed.

As he saw the Indian carriers bearing their *petates* [grass mats], from the near-by lake to the marketplace, Fray Marcos was reminded of his first coming into the Village of the Mats, Petatlán, on the historic journey northward. Here in Xochimilco the Indians wove reed mats similar to those which covered the houses of Petatlán. But already the memory of these things seemed to belong to the centuries past.

Fray Marcos was beginning to long for the peace of his blessed Father Francis who rested now in the beautiful church named for him, which Brother Elias had built.

He thought that he would like to repose at the last in the city of Mexico, where so many whom he had known and revered in life, servants of Christ and of their country, were laid at rest.

With his helpless fingers he could not write a letter, asking his provincial for this last favor. The message was conveyed by another.

Missionary, pioneer, herald of His Majesty and of the noble viceroy, Fray Marcos de Niza asked that he might be removed to Mexico City, and there, when he should have passed into the next life, interred "with the ancient holy ones."

His provincial was happy to grant the request.

In Mexico City Fray Marcos renewed memories still more poignant than those of Jalapa or Xochimilco. Memories of his meeting with Viceroy Mendoza, after the beloved Bishop de Zumárraga had brought the friar to the latter with the recommendation that he be entrusted with the important mission of reconnaisance in the northern countries. Memories of Alvar Núñez Cabeza de Vaca, whose powerful recital had moved the viceroy to institute the search for the golden cities. One of Núñez' three companions, Estevan the Moor, had identified himself with the momentous venture in a way Fray Marcos de Niza could never forget. Somewhere in the inhospitable pueblo of Hawikuh the bones of that unfortunate slave were rotting — but for his disobedience and concupiscence the whole outcome of the expedition might have been different.

Memories there were of the valiant young Don Francisco Vásquez de Coronado — Coronado, who had disappointed Mendoza, his chief, in his conduct of the expedition, although Fray Marcos believed the young general had tried to do his best. . . .

Memories of Bishop Juan — the man of God whose

best monument endured after him in the Christian lives of the thousands of Indians whom he had been instrumental in converting to the true faith, and the thriving works of Christian charity and education he had established. But to Fray Marcos de Niza, not less than any of these deeds was the bishop's magnificent trust and kindliness to a disillusioned and grief-stricken friar, whom the world looked upon in scorn.

Of all these men in high places and in lowly, Fray Marcos de Niza alone remained, in that year of our Lord, 1558. Their lives had been filled with momentous incidents, with thrilling adventure, with many successes as well as solicitudes and disappointments. History would note their record and posterity would praise or censure them according to its judgment on their deeds. Fray Marcos knew at last, if he had not known it before, that they were all no more than children, playing the game of life as they deemed it should be played. Like children, they had wearied after awhile and settled down to rest.

Remembering that the day had been long and garish, and that repose is sweet to a tired man, Fray Marcos de Niza folded his chaplet over his hands, withered and misshapen by the dread paralysis, breathed a prayer, and closed his eyes that he might shut out the glare of the desert of this world. . . .